To Tony.

With best wishes from

Grandad. 1953. Xmas

"Keep moving!" Wyatt called to the coach driver

Great
COWBOY
ADVENTURES

EDITED BY PETER BARING

With Drawings by Geoffrey Whittam

THE HEIRLOOM LIBRARY
LONDON

COPYRIGHT
THE HEIRLOOM LIBRARY

Printed and bound in Great Britain for
HEIRLOOM LIBRARY LIMITED
by Jarrold and Sons Limited, Norwich

CONTENTS

LIST OF COLOUR PLATES

INTRODUCTION

This is a collection of stirring tales about the old Wild West. They tell of the wild life that was lived by the men who trekked west across the Missouri River to explore the prairies beyond. A thousand miles west of the great river rise the foot-hills of the Rocky Mountains, the pine-covered skirt of the snow-clad peaks. On the other side of the mountain barrier are the fertile valleys of California, sloping down towards the sun-bathed shore of the Pacific Ocean.

When the American pioneers crossed the Missouri all the lands between the river and the mountains were populated by the Red Indians—more than three million of them, living by hunting buffaloes, occasionally settling long enough to grow a crop of corn. On the other side of the mountains the rich land of California had long been annexed by the King of Spain, whose soldiers had also conquered the whole of Mexico. A hundred and thirty years ago the Spaniards in Mexico revolted against their home country; they set up an independent State, and California became one of its provinces.

That was a hundred and thirty years ago. Within sixty years from that time the American pioneers had almost exterminated

7

the three million Redskins and the great buffalo herds that roamed wild over the prairies. They had driven the Mexicans out of California and Texas, and had declared both provinces to be States of the Union.

The American conquest of the western prairies makes one of the greatest tales in history. This conquest was not made by a trained, disciplined army. It was made by hundreds of small commandos—some twenty strong, some consisting of no more than one man with a gun, an axe and a pick. These pioneers marched west to look for land. They were determined to seize the land with their gun, prepared to clear it with their axe, ready to mine it with their pick. For rumour said that great seams of gold and silver lay beneath the fields of Western America.

The pioneers fought not only the Indians and the Mexicans; they fought each other—for possession of the best land, the fattest cattle and the richest seams of gold. They raided each other's ranches, stole each other's cattle, flooded each other's gold diggings. Yet, though driven on by the spur for wealth, these men—the cowboys and the miners—had a code of honour higher than exists in many a civilized country. They would always open their homes and share their meal with a stranger, they would never rob a guest; they might shoot to kill, but they would never shoot a man without a gun. The only man to whom they showed no mercy was the cheat.

Great Cowboy Adventures is a collection of stories about some well- and some lesser-known heroes of the Wild West. Kit Carson and General Custer are names familiar to everyone who has followed Western films; Wyatt Earp, the hero of the first story in this book, is famous, too. He was the ace of all sheriffs, and without doubt the smartest shot in the whole Wild West.

How Tombstone came to get its name is the subject of another story, the tale of Ed Schiefflin's mine. They say that the better part of five million men tried their luck digging for gold and silver in the far west. There must have been something wrong with the dealing of the cards of fate; so many of them turned up in Ed's pack!

Another redoubtable sheriff was old Ira Aten. There has been less written about him than he deserves. His methods were the model for all subsequent story-book detectives. How he picked

8

out the culprit behind the cattle-rustling campaign that nearly ruined the enormous XIT ranch is a story that should prove excellent exercise for those who like guessing "who done it?"

John Marsh has always been one of those characters against whom the historians have put a question-mark. Was he a traitor, an American secret service man, a greedy crook or self-sacrificing patriot? Sent down from Harvard University for rowdyism when he was half-way through his medical course, he got a job as Indian interpreter to Governor Cass, the Special Commissioner for Indian territories. After being mainly responsible for defeating Chief Black Hawk and for annexing four new States to the Union he had to disappear quickly, as there was talk of prosecuting him for selling guns secretly to the very Indians he was supposed to have been fighting. A few years later he turned up in the Mexican province of California. The rest of his story is published here in a new and extremely unexpected version.

As for the remaining tale, it is about one, Harry Adams. You may not have heard of him; he was not very famous. He was just one of those men who flourished for a day like a gourd in the desert. All that is left of his stage-coach empire is the memory that once upon a time the Adams expresses fought an overland battle with Wells, Fargo Co. for the monopoly of the pony trails.

PETER BARING

SILVER AND LEAD

He hung his broad-brimmed hat on a nail in the wall. With a look of faint distaste he surveyed the room. He had just paid Johnny Behan one month's rent in advance for that room: three hundred and fifty dollars was a fair packet to have to pay for one room with unpainted mud walls and no furniture. But that one room was a whole house with a front and back door and a roof of its own, and whole houses in Tombstone, Arizona, in 1880 cost big money.

It was less than a year since Ed Schiefflin had turned up the sod of earth which covered the pure silver lode upon which the town of Tombstone was built. In that year Ed had become a millionaire, and Tombstone had grown from one inhabitant to over five thousand. From east and west and north prospectors, saloon owners, store-keepers had come pouring on to the rock plateau 5000 feet above the sandy, scrub-strewn desert of Arizona. With them came the card-sharpers, the bank-robbers and the cattle-rustlers. A town built on silver meant good money, easy money, quick money.

John P. Clum, the new tenant on 2 Fremont Street, was not a prospector nor a card-sharper. He did not know exactly what he was; he had done so many things in his life. His last job had been Head of the San Carlos Apache Indian Reserve, a Federal appointment. For a couple of years he had rode up and down his territory keeping law and order, adding to an already growing reputation for good administration and unshakeable honesty. But the work had grown humdrum, and Clum had adventure in his blood. He turned in his resignation to the Governor. A week later he bedded at the new Cosmopolitan Hotel at Tombstone, the town's first two-storey building.

What Clum found in Tombstone both annoyed and captivated him. He was a man who believed in good government: Tombstone had no government at all—the nearest peace officer was seventy-five miles away at Tucson. The thought of a town in which everybody did as he pleased, including digging a silver mine plumb in the middle of the main street, was too much for John P. Clum—it was a challenge which could not be resisted.

11

Tombstone already had a newspaper: the *Nugget* it was called. Clum had sat at the hotel bar turning over its four badly set pages. There was mighty little news in it. The point of the pages was the editorial, splashed in heavily leaded type in a box on the front page. Clum read the editorial and he read it again. Then he called for a drink: he felt that he needed it. He had never read such infuriating balderdash in his life. Here was a newspaper actually telling its readers that it would be suicide for the town to have a Mayor, Council, Treasurer or Marshal. It would strangle the development of the silver industry: so wrote the editor.

Clum was a man who made up his mind quickly. If that is going to be the editorial policy of the *Nugget*, he said to himself, I'm entering the newspaper business. Five minutes later he announced his intention to the company assembled in the bar.

A tall, broad-shouldered man with a drooping tawny moustache came over to Clum. "That's talk I like to hear, stranger," he said. "What are you going to call the paper?"

"Every tombstone needs an epitaph, I guess," Clum replied straight off the reel. The old-stagers at the bar guffawed at the sally of polished wit. "Epitaph!" They rolled the word round their tongues and swallowed it with the whisky.

"Yeah!" said the tall man. "I reckon that's a mighty fine name. Here's to the *Tombstone Epitaph*!" He jerked his glass to his mouth and downed a mouthful of yellow liquid. "I give you a toast, gentlemen—the *Tombstone Epitaph*!" The toast echoed round the room.

Clum engaged the toast-master in conversation; there was a lot that he wanted to know about the town where he had just decided to found a newspaper. Coming to that, there was a lot that he needed to know about how to run a newspaper; it was about the one thing in his career that he had never done. But the tall man with a drooping moustache knew very little about either subject. He had only just arrived in town that afternoon, and ever since he had been old enough to jump on to the saddle he had made a living with a gun. When it came to pens, he could sign his name and that was about all.

"By the way," Clum asked, "what name do you go by?"

"Wyatt Earp."

"You don't say!" Clum put down his glass on the counter. "I've been wanting to meet you for a long time. They told me that you had gone to Deadwood, Dakota, as Marshal. What made you come on here?"

"Just wanderlust. I thought that I couldn't let Ed Schiefflin get away with all the silver in Arizona, so I reckoned I'd try my hand at prospecting."

"That's out of your line?" Clum inquired.

"My line's anything straight," Earp replied.

A week later Earp had been sworn in as Deputy Sheriff of Tombstone district of Pima County, Arizona, and the first edition of the *Epitaph* was being snatched up by the eager citizens of the boom-town.

It was not any affection for law and order that made Sheriff Charles Shibell of Tucson take Earp as deputy. Shibell confined his duties to keeping guard on the Tucson calaboose; as he never bothered to arrest anyone, it was not a very arduous job. The only catch about it from Shibell's angle was that his pay was due to come out of the taxes he was meant to collect. As half the inhabitants of the seventy-five thousand square miles of Pima County never dreamed of paying taxes, and that half included all the citizens of Tombstone, Shibell reckoned that something had got to be done about it. Only he was not the man for doing things. What he wanted, he reckoned, was a good assistant.

When Charley Shibell got word that Wyatt Earp, the man who had tamed turbulent Wichita and Dodge City, was in Tombstone, he rode up and offered Wyatt the job at five hundred dollars a month plus commission on taxes collected. Wyatt took an hour to think it over. He had spent the last five years as a peace officer; he was hoping to have closed that chapter in his life. But five hundred dollars were five hundred dollars, and living in a boom-town where a night's lodging cost ten dollars was expensive.

"I'll take your job," Wyatt told Shibell.

The first editorial of the *Epitaph* congratulated Tombstone on its fortune in having as its law officer a man whose name was famous all over the United States. "Let us express the conviction that before long it will be as safe to walk down the sidewalks of Tombstone as it is in New York or Boston," Clum wrote in the forthright style that was to make his paper sell out within an hour of printing.

Sprawling in the one and only chair in the office of the *Nugget*, Old Man Clanton uttered a stream of unprintable oaths. Since the stream of Clanton's blasphemy was as regular as water flowing down to sea no one paid any attention.

"Didn't you hear me?" Old Man Clanton rose to his feet, sending the chair sprawling and flinging to the floor the paper which he was reading.

"What's biting you?" Woods looked up from the tray where he was setting the type for the *Nugget*'s next edition.

"I'm not having no swashbuckling, tea-drinking, holy-as-Mary Earps in this town. The man's a menace!"

"What do you reckon to do about it?" inquired the type-setter, who was also editor, reporter, circulation manager and feature writer.

"You're going to do something about it!" Clanton stamped his hob-nailed forty-gallon boot on the floor. "You're going to print an editorial demanding that a new county be set up here at Tombstone with its own Sheriff, and I'll see that the new Sheriff takes his orders from us. I'll make Johnny Behan Sheriff, and his first job will be to run Earp out of town as a suspicious character."

The next morning the *Nugget* came out with an editorial that made Tombstone's citizens glow with pride. Henry Woods proved conclusively that Tombstone was the most important, thriving, flourishing, enterprising, famous town in the United States. "It is unthinkable that Tombstone should not be a county seat," the editor concluded. "This very day a body of the town's most respected burghers headed by 'Old Man' Clanton himself rides to Prescott to lay our town's request before Governor Fremont."

Clum lapped up the words of his rival's editorial. "So, the *Nugget*'s coming out for government at last," he muttered to himself. "About time too."

Earp strode in from the street, his Sheriff's badge shining on his chest.

"Seen the *Nugget*?" Clum asked.

"Yeah! I saw Clanton and his gang ride out of town on the way up here. They're reckoning on the Governor making

Johnny Behan Sheriff. There can't be elections until the new county has been established a year, and the Governor makes the first appointment of Sheriff."

"Why don't you run, Wyatt?"

"I wouldn't have a chance with Clanton lobbying for Behan."

"I know Fremont fairly well." Clum was pacing up and down the eight-foot room: he always thought better on his feet. "I reckon I'll cable him."

"Just as you think, J.P." Wyatt had come to recognize Clum as a friend to be trusted.

A few days later Johnny Behan ran into Earp on the sidewalk outside the Cosmopolitan Hotel.

"Come into the bar, Wyatt. I want a word with you."

"I'm thirsty myself," Earp replied, and led the way through the swing door. He ordered a tumbler of whisky for Behan and a lemonade for himself.

Johnny Behan put his cards on the table. If Clum kept up the pressure to have Earp made Sheriff neither of the two would get the job. The Governor would appoint a compromise candidate.

"We can split the job between us, if you get Clum to call off the campaign. I'll have the Sheriff's badge and make you deputy. We'll split the fees fifty-fifty. I'll look after the civil side, and you can take over the criminal. Deputize as many men as you like to help you."

"That suits me, Johnny," Wyatt answered. "The Wells, Fargo outfit have offered me a job to ride with the bullion expresses. I couldn't hold that job at the same time as being County Sheriff."

"Jack-a-crack!" Behan raised his glass. "Let's drink to it."

Behan rode off to the State capital at Prescott and came back to Tombstone as Sheriff. The first thing that he did was to swear in William Breakenridge as Deputy and Henry Woods as Assistant Deputy. Earp caught his breath as he heard of the double-cross. He would have gone round and had it out with Behan there and then if he had not been holding a telegram. It came from the United States Marshal of Arizona, offering him the Deputy's job at seven hundred dollars a month, two hundred more than he had been getting as Deputy Sheriff. Wyatt walked straight round to the cable company's office and sent off a wire taking the job as Deputy Federal Marshal with duty to guard the mails in and out of Tombstone.

For the next weeks Earp rode alongside the Wells, Fargo coaches, shotgun in hand. Never once did the Clanton gang try a hold-up. One evening Virgil and Morgan, Wyatt's brothers, came into Tombstone. The three Earps spent some time looking for lodgings where they could set up home. The Wells, Fargo agent sent over to Wyatt to tell him that the bullion coach was due to leave in an hour.

"I reckon I'll send someone else to ride along tonight. Me and my brothers are having a reunion."

By next morning Tombstone buzzed with the news that the express had been held up in Deadman's Gulch, and that the outlaws had got away with twenty-five thousand dollars' worth of silver.

Wyatt fastened on his gun-belt and tested his two six-shooters for speed of draw. Taking his brothers with him, he galloped out of town on the Tucson trail. In the gulch he came on a litter of cartridge cases marking the spot of the hold-up. Off to the east was a line of fresh hoof-prints. Wyatt jerked the reins.

"Looks like three of them did the job. I'll lay even money that Curly Bill and Ike Clanton were two, and I wouldn't be surprised if Frank Stilwell's the third."

"Hasn't Behan sworn in Stilwell as a Deputy Sheriff?" asked Virgil.

"Doesn't make a dime of difference in this county, Virg." Wyatt spurred his horse to get more speed. When they came to Seven Rings water-hole they saw horses strung to the tree. Wyatt rode slightly ahead of his two brothers.

"You're under arrest," he shouted.

"Who d'you think you are?" Frank Stilwell stood with his hands on his hips a few inches above his holsters.

"You know well enough, Frank. Get those hands up!"

"What are you arresting us for?" Stilwell slowly raised his hands.

"For robbing the Tucson coach last night." Wyatt dismounted sharply and walked over to Stilwell. With two quick movements he jerked the outlaw's six-shooters on to the sand. Virgil and Morgan had the other two men covered with their shotguns.

16

The express had been held up at Deadman's Gulch

17

The Earps led the three disarmed men back to Tombstone. The Judge was having dinner. He sent word to say that he would come over to the courthouse in half an hour. By that time fifty men had poured into the tiny courtroom. Behan was there, surrounded by his friends. He had been standing at the corner of Fremont and Fifth when Earp and the outlaws had ridden by.

Judge Spicer rapped his gavel on the desk for silence. The prosecution case had been given. Wyatt had proved that the spent cartridges fitted the outlaws' guns. "What is the defence?" called the Judge.

Johnny Behan went into the witness stand.

"Your Honour!" he testified. "These three men were playing faro with me at the Oriental until six o'clock this morning. They weren't anywhere near the Tucson coach."

"Any further witnesses for the defence?" asked the Judge.

Johnny Ringo pushed his way forward. He did not bother to go into the stand.

"Sure. I saw these boys tie up their horses next to mine last evening and the broncs were still there when I fetched mine this morning."

The Judge turned to Earp. "It looks as if you pulled in the wrong boys, Wyatt. Case is dismissed."

Next morning the *Nugget* came out with an editorial under the headline: "Where was Marshal Earp when the Tucson coach was shot up?" John Clum had no difficulty in understanding the inference of the article, as he sat sucking his pencil considering what he should write in his own editorial. He thought for a moment and started writing swiftly: "Marshal Wyatt Earp is the one honest man in this town of twisters."

Wyatt and his brothers were having breakfast when Doc Holliday called through the window: "Johnny Behan's got a warrant out for you, Wyatt. Three of his boys have laid affidavits that you shot up the Tucson coach. You are charged with the murder of a passenger."

"He can't do that." Wyatt gulped down the rest of his coffee and pushed back his chair.

"If I were you, I'd clear out of town for a few days," Doc said.

"I'm doing no such thing." Wyatt pulled down the brim of

18

his tall, black Stetson. "I'm going straight over to the court to surrender. We'll see what the Judge has got to say."

Behan had been caught unprepared. His witnesses were still bleary-eyed from their drink the night before. Only one of them could remember having signed an affidavit, and *he* admitted that he had not read the paper.

"Case dismissed." Judge Spicer banged his gavel. "I'm getting a bit tired of dismissing cases," he added. "Ain't anyone ever going to prove anything in this court?"

Wyatt strolled over to the *Epitaph* office. Clum was turning the rolling handle of his press. The two men talked for a while. After Earp had gone out Clum pulled the type tray off the machine, tore up the sheets already printed and started again with pencil and paper.

Wyatt and his brother, Morg, were strolling down Fremont Street when Jack Reigebaum came out of the Oriental gambling-rooms.

"Wyatt!" he called. "I want you to take in a bum from inside of here. He's got his sleeve stuffed with aces."

"What's his name?"

"I don't know, but the boys here have seen him before. They call him 'Johnny-behind-the-Deuce'."

"Oh! that tinhorn." Wyatt was already half-way through the door. "He used to play his tricks in Dodge City, way back in '77. I'll have him in the calaboose for a day or two."

Wyatt pulled the bolt on the door of the only cell in the Tombstone County Jail. He twisted the key twice and then hooked it on to his watch chain. "What's all that shindy?" he said to himself. He quickened his pace and made for the centre of the town. Doc Holliday met him as he hurried along.

"Best get back to the calaboose and hand out that tinhorn you've got in there," was the advice of the dentist.

"What's up?" inquired Earp.

"The cowboys are in town today, and they reckon on stringing up Johnny-behind-the-Deuce for a spot of entertainment. Some of them have lost a lot of money in the Oriental."

"Oh! So that's it. Thank's for the tip, Doc."

When Wyatt came into Allen Street he saw a crowd of five hundred swarming up the wide, dust-covered avenue. He dug his heels in the grit and brought his shotgun up to his shoulder.

"Get out of the way," yelled the crowd. "This is a lynching."

Wyatt said nothing. In the crowd, in addition to a bunch of drunk, wild cowpunchers were several hundred miners. In the front of the crowd was Dick Gird, Ed Schiefflin's partner in the Lucky Cuss mine.

"Dick," Wyatt called out, "I'm pointing this gun at you. Take your boys home. This ain't business for you."

One of the cowboys shouted back: "This ain't business, Earp. This is death, if you don't get out of the way."

"If I go, eighteen of you will come with me," was the reply. "There are eighteen shots in this gun and everyone will hit a mark. Dick, you're the first."

At other times Wyatt and Dick Gird were on the best of terms. It took a fearless Marshal to point his gun straight at a friend. Dick knew that Wyatt was a man who meant what he said. He turned and started to push his way through the crowd. Some of the miners followed him. Without another word being said or a shot being fired, the lynch mob dispersed. The cowboys thought better of the plan. After all, there were other ways of making pleasure in Tombstone.

Wyatt slung his gun over his shoulder. "There's too much doing in this town," he said later to Clum. "What Tombstone needs is a police force under its own Marshal. I've got my work cut out guarding the mails and the bullion."

Clum agreed. But it wasn't so easy, he countered. Any decent candidate for Mayor or town councilman would be opposed by a nominee of the Clanton gang. The *Epitaph* editor doubted if honest men could be found who would stand for office.

Wyatt hummed. He was of the same opinion; but something had got to be done. "How's the newspaper campaign going?"

"It's brought in a thousand dollars," Clum replied, pulling open the drawer of his desk to show Wyatt the heap of green-backs.

"We'll need more than that to fight an election," was Wyatt's only comment as he slammed the door behind him. A piece of mud fell off the wall on top of the next editorial of the *Epitaph*.

"This town's enough to make any man a killer." John Clum brushed away the mess from the sheet of paper.

Wyatt pinned deputies' badges on his two brothers and enrolled Doc Holliday into his small force of law officers. At that same time Sheriff Behan could call on a posse of twelve deputies, all of them trigger-happy and most of them outlaws. If there was to be a head-on collision between the Federal Marshal and the County Sheriff the scales would be tipped heavily in Behan's favour.

But for the time being at any rate Behan wanted to remain on reasonably good terms with Earp. Occasionally he discussed business matters with Wyatt, and once he even went so far as to get the County Treasurer, another of Clanton's stooges, to pay Wyatt a couple of hundred dollars horse allowance.

Old Man Clanton, meanwhile, was continuing his reign of terror over the ranch land of Cochise and Pima counties. Night after night his riders would go out; morning after morning they would come in driving a herd of stolen steers before them. The cattlemen dared not fight back; resistance to the Clanton gang meant instantaneous death. Underground there was formed an Arizona Cattlemen's Protection Association. A rancher who unwittingly mentioned in a Tombstone saloon that he belonged to the association was found hanging next day from the bougainvillea tree in front of his homestead.

Clanton ran his own butchery business in Tombstone. Every ounce of meat eaten by everyone of the population, already swollen to ten thousand, had been hacked off the carcass of a stolen steer. It was common knowledge in the town; so was the fate of Ed Hartwell who tried to run a butcher's shop selling honest meat. Ed was tied on to the hind quarters of a stallion and dragged in the dust down Fremont Street. The next day what was left of him was loaded on to the Tucson stage-coach.

But the prize of a fully loaded bullion coach was more tempting than cattle-rustling. That was why Clanton had settled his gang in and around Tombstone. That was why he had taken in John Ringo and Curly Bill on a twenty-five per cent cut each. They knew as much about stage-robbing as Jesse James himself.

Curly Bill took up position in a shack that lay off the Bisbee road. He let it be known in Tombstone that any coach that wanted to go to Bisbee must pay him a toll of a thousand dollars. The price of refusal was to be the confiscation of the pay-load and the murder of the passengers. As soon as Wells, Fargo's head office in San Fransisco had considered the offer, the

21

company cabled to Wyatt authorizing him to engage any number of assistants deemed necessary to protect their coaches.

The next time that Curly Bill tried to hold up the Bisbee stage he found himself facing a force of half a dozen of the best shots in the west. Curly Bill was not much of a shot himself, but he had with him Tom and Frank MacLowery who could each hit a dime at fifty yards. The MacLowerys fired, but Wyatt and his brothers fired a shade quicker. Curly Bill felt the lead dig into his neck, and the burning smell of charred flesh made him sick.

"Back!" he shouted.

Wyatt fired again. A horse whinnied in death agony.

"Keep moving!" Wyatt called to the coach driver. The coach thundered on its way, leaving the Earps in command of the valley and the Clanton gang riding full-tilt for shelter.

The news that the stage hold-up had failed caused a wave of excitement in Tombstone. It had just been decided to set up a municipal government, and elections were pending. The traders in the town approached Wyatt to take on the job of Town Sheriff at a higher rate of pay than the federal job and the Wells, Fargo appointment combined. Wyatt felt that he could not hand over his two jobs so soon; he suggested that Virgil be offered the town appointment. Clanton put up one of his men to run against Virgil, and poured money into the miners' pockets to get them to vote against Clum's so-called Law-and-Order Party.

There was trouble brewing in the town as the elections approached. Behan made it clear that as County Sheriff he intended to keep order. What that meant Clum and the Earps knew only too well. A bunch of cowmen rode up and down the streets firing off six-shooters all through the night.

The *Nugget* announced that never before had Tombstone known such peace and quiet. Its editorial attacked the Law-and-Order Party, saying that they only wanted to get into power to establish a reign of oppression; this was a reference to the party's proposed by-laws to forbid anyone but a peace officer to carry a gun within the town limits.

The *Epitaph* replied in kind with a history of the recent stage hold-ups, listing the men engaged in each attack. At least half of them were Clanton candidates for posts in the administration. The night after that edition of the *Epitaph* had come out the first of the town's bad fires broke out. It swept down the street of log and mud cabins, caught alight the dried straw roof of the *Epitaph* building and set up such an inferno of heat inside that the type was melted like butter in a frying-pan.

On election day Behan deputized no less than a hundred men in the gang's pay to keep "order" at the polling stations. The Law-and-Order Party countered by putting two of their men on for every one of Behan's. The only difference between the two armies of election officers was that Johnny Behan charged the county funds twenty dollars a head for each one of his deputies.

When the votes came to be counted the Clanton candidates had a small majority. Wyatt had watched the papers being taken out of the ballot boxes. No less than 134 had been taken out of the Galeyville box where the cowmen living in the San Simon Valley voted; 133 of these votes were for the Clanton man, 1 for Virgil. And yet Wyatt knew for a fact that not more than fifty men lived in the valley.

"We're claiming a recount," he announced. "Seal up the ballots again; we're having them sent to the State Board of Elections."

Behan smiled over the table: "Don't know when you're licked, do you, Wyatt?"

"Guess I never did," the Marshal replied.

"Okay," Behan said offhandedly. "You can have the votes sent up to the board, but we run the town in the meanwhile."

Outside, the gathered crowd of drunk Clanton cowpunchers discharged their guns and called for a whisky barrel to be brought out to them. They were going to celebrate.

Men who were in Tombstone that night will never forget it. Clanton's men were drunk with more than power. Johnny Ringo went into Smith's Piccadilly Bar to stoke up, and little Ed Hawkins offered to stand him a can of beer.

"Don't you know I only drink whisky?" Ringo expected no answer: he just shot Ed dead. Out in the streets horses without riders clattered and whinnied; some of the boys had thought it a joke to untie every horse in town. The young Clantons had dragged a piano out into the sidewalk and were having the time of their life making Big-nosed Kate, Doc Holliday's wife, dance on top of it.

John Clum sent for Wyatt Earp.

"Wyatt, you've got to mount a guard in this office, otherwise it won't last out the night," he begged the Marshal.

The *Epitaph* had re-established itself in a stable at the far end of town.

Wyatt snapped back the hammer of his six-shooter and sent the barrel spinning. He slipped a slug with the sixth chamber —the one next to the hammer that he usually kept empty for safety.

"I've had a better idea than that, J.P."

"What's that?"

"Morg and Virgil are opening a bar outside the courthouse. We're serving free drinks."

"Have you lost your head, Wyatt?" Clum came to a full stop in his pacing and stared Earp full in the eyes.

"On the contrary, J.P. Give me half an hour and you'll see who is mad."

Doc Holliday rubbed his hands dry.

"That should just about do it," he said as he gave a kick to the barrel and sent it careering across the yard.

"What's that for, Doc?" Morg asked.

"Just to mix it in." Doc Holliday pushed a couple of bottles into the pockets of his greatcoat. "Get that barrel tapped and set it up, boys."

Morgan and Virgil carried the barrel out into the street. Someone brought out a supply of glasses. From nowhere the crowd assembled.

"Hurry up, Morg," Ringo shouted. "I've shot one man tonight for giving me the wrong drink."

"This ought to suit you," Morg replied, handing the mug over the head of a cowboy who had fallen in a stupor with his head against the barrel.

It was not long before the demand for free drinks slackened. All along the street men were leaning against the sides of houses, doubled up, reaching into the gutter.

"My head, my head," whined Ringo.

"It's my inside," gurgled Ike Clanton between bouts of sickness.

Wyatt Earp surveyed the scene with satisfaction.

"Doc," he called. "You're a fumbled-handed lout when it

comes to pulling out teeth, but you're a bloomin' wonder at mixing medicine."

Meanwhile the presses of the *Epitaph* were able to roll without interruption. When it came out the editorial was so sizzling hot that Old Man Clanton screwed it up and threw it on to the floor after reading the first paragraph

"WAKE UP, TOMBSTONE

or you will all be in one. This town is the scandal of America. A gang of blood-thirsty, murderous thieves has seized control of the administration by fraud. We call on every citizen who believes in living another twenty-four hours to report to the Cosmopolitan Hotel and join a force of Vigilantes. A Committee of Safety has been formed to raise and train volunteers that will help Wyatt Earp and his deputies keep the law."

"That Earp has got to be got rid of," was Clanton's decision.

"If you say so, boss," Ike, his son, commented.

"I've said so before, but none of you yellow-livered skunks has done anything about it." His father spat out a wad of tobacco.

"We'll finish off the Earps this time." Ike took down a gun from the wall. "Come on, boys. Who's following me?"

His brother Billy, the two MacLowerys and Billy Claiborne trooped out of the room behind him. Their heads were still splitting from Doc Holliday's concoction. They were feeling the need to take the scum off their tongues with a tone-up of Scotch. In the Piccadilly Bar their tongues recovered soon enough; they started wagging of what they would do to the Earps when they caught sight of them.

Colonel Hooker, Tombstone's leading attorney, was in the Piccadilly while all this was going on. The Clanton boys did not notice him sliding out through the window.

"Wyatt!" The Colonel came into the Cosmopolitan shouting at the top of his voice. "Wyatt! Where have you gotten yourself?"

"Calm down, old-timer!" Wyatt appeared in the passageway behind Hooker's back. "What's biting you?"

"The Clanton boys are down at the Piccadilly; they're telling the whole saloon that they are on the way up to kill all the Earps."

Wyatt was pulling on his shirt. "Do you reckon they mean it?" he asked as soon as his head emerged through the collar.

"What d'you think I'd come running up here for otherwise?" Colonel Hooker stamped his foot on the floor in desperation.

"Thought you might like some exercise after breakfast," mumbled Wyatt. "All the same, many thanks, Colonel. Just you wait till me and my brothers have had a cup of coffee."

Breakfast that morning was eaten somewhat hurriedly despite Wyatt's efforts to keep to a normal pace: his brothers had one eye on their plate and the other out of the window. They were just bracing on their guns when who should come in but Doc Holliday. Morgan shot a look of inquiry at Wyatt: should they tell Doc what was happening?

Doc gave no time to Wyatt to answer. "The first job our new town council will have to tackle is to clean up the sick on the sidewalks." At that the dishevelled dentist slapped his ample paunch and roared with laughter.

"Sure, sure," Wyatt replied absent-mindedly. "Say, Virg, don't take that rifle of yours: this is a job for six-shooters."

"What job?" Doc turned round to face Virgil.

Virgil, who could kill a man before he had got the second word out of his mouth, was at a loss for what to say.

"This ain't your business, Doc," Wyatt intervened.

"How come you know what is and what isn't my business, Wyatt Earp?" inquired Doc with a show of righteous indignation. "I'd have you know that in my time I've been in every kind of business from drug-pedalling to show business. If it's fighting that you're thinking of, I tell you I'm half Irish and I'm damned if I'm going to be left out of a fight."

"What are we going to do with him?" asked Wyatt hopelessly.

"Take him along, I guess," Virgil replied. "It won't do no harm to have a medical man just in case we want a few auty-popsies or whatever-they-call-'em done on some dead'uns."

"All right, Doc. String along behind. Got your pea-shooter with you?"

Doc nodded. They stuffed their pockets with extra ammo, and then set out down Fremont Street. On their way they ran into Johnny Behan. The County Sheriff was leaning against the side of the Occidental Hotel, which was where he lodged when in Tombstone.

"You look as if you're going places, Wyatt," he spoke out of the corner of his mouth without troubling to remove his cigar.

"I think you had better come with us, Sheriff," Wyatt said firmly. "There are five men in this town who are arranging murder. It would be kind of nice if the County Sheriff were to be present when they were arrested."

"If you're referring to Billy and Ike Clanton and the Mac-Lowery boys, they're not armed. They don't mean no trouble."

"How about your coming along to check up?"

"You do your own dirty work, Earp. I've got other things to look after." Behan spat out the cigar and turned into the hotel.

Wyatt called his brothers and Doc to move on. "He ain't worth lick spittle."

"I'll bet he runs straight through that hotel passage," volunteered Doc, "and comes out the other side into Allen Street and legs it down to the Clantons to say that we're on the way."

"I'll not take that bet, Doc," was Wyatt's comment, as he strode down the street.

At the corner of Fremont and Fourth the posse ran into a crowd of townsfolk. Colonel Hooker was at their head.

"Wyatt!" he called. "Quit marching off as if the west wind was on your tail. Meet Tombstone's Vigilantes; these are the boys who responded to the appeal in the *Epitaph* and reported at the Cosmopolitan this morning. Ike Elam has dished them out a gun each from his shop. I've taught 'em how to salute. Now they're ready to take care of the Clanton boys."

"Now, look here, Colonel." Wyatt was none too pleased. "This affair is between the Clanton gang and the Earps. There's no call for anyone else to get himself killed."

"What's Tombstone going to do if you get killed?" asked Ike Elam.

"When that day comes, Mr. Elam, you can pack up and go back east; there won't be no silver left in the Lucky Cuss."

At that time the Lucky Cuss Mine was turning out an average of thirty thousand dollars a day of pure silver, and the idea that the supply would ever come to an end was quite unthinkable. Wyatt set off, and the other three followed.

"They're in the O.K. Corral," shouted one of the Vigilantes.

27

The corral was a yard where cowpunchers could tie up their broncs overnight; the proprietor undertook to give them a feed and a wash-down. Leaning against its fence was none other than Johnny Behan. Sure enough he had done exactly what Doc had feared.

Wyatt came to a halt in front of the County Sheriff. "Johnny!" he said ironically, "you've got a habit of cropping up in places like mushrooms. You wouldn't be waiting for someone to pick you?"

Behan drew himself up. "I'm telling you, Earp, these men are not armed. If you go into the corral and there is any gun-play, I'll go straight over to the courthouse and swear out a warrant against you for murder."

Just at that precise moment a bullet whizzed straight through the space between Wyatt and Behan. The latter took his cue and ran along the fence and into the first door.

"I thought you said that they were unarmed, Johnny!" Wyatt called after him, but there was no answer. "Come on, boys! We're going in."

They marched through the gate, their hands on their holsters. Inside, the five men had taken up position to cover each other with their fire. Billy Clanton was standing behind a horse-cart that was parked near the bottom end of the yard.

"You don't take another step, Earp," he shouted in his rather squeaky voice.

"Which Earp are you talking to?"

"The lot of you," replied Clanton. "Stay where you are. I'm giving you one last chance. You get on three of the horses tied up here and ride out of town and *stay out*. Otherwise . . ."

"Otherwise what?" asked Wyatt.

"Otherwise I'll blow your brains out on to these paving stones."

"That's daring talk for a yellow rat." Wyatt determined to be insulting; making a man lose his temper was one way of getting him to shoot off-mark. Clanton was no exception; he fired off both his guns from the hip. The bullets went wide and notched into the fence near the gate.

"You asked for this," was Wyatt's only comment as he watched his Buntline Special, the gun with the extra long silver barrel, discharge straight into Clanton's chest.

28

With that the battle began. The deputies hurled themselves towards whatever cover there was. Morg found an old creosote barrel; Doc went behind the wooden support of an overhanging roof; Virgil dodged behind a horse. There was enough noise to waken the night-shift of miners—and they sleep like the dead. People raced up to the entrance to see what it was all about. The horses strained at their ropes with terror.

But the noise was soon over. The Earps were better shots than the outlaw gang. The Clantons may have boasted in their day, but they were bettered in this fight. Wyatt was firing both his guns at once with deadly accuracy. Frank MacLowery pitched and stumbled with a bullet in his groin. His brother Tom snapped at his trigger, but the chambers were empty. Too impetuous to unload, he hurled the empty weapon at Wyatt's head before reaching for his rifle. The throw missed; while Tom was unguarded, Morg took deadly aim and shot him between the eyes. But even as Morg turned to face the next of his enemies he heard an agonizing cry from his brother Virgil. A piece of lead had travelled straight through his calf to the bone.

From the number of cartridge cases found afterwards in the yard it looked as if the battle had gone on for hours. In reality it was all over in two to three minutes, before ever the crowd outside the gate had summoned up a decision on how to intervene. The Earps commanded O.K. Corral. Billy Claiborne had dodged along the wall of the building at the side of the yard and slipped through a door. Ike Clanton, too, had escaped.

"Why did you let Clanton go?" Morg asked his elder brother.

"I ain't never shot a man without a gun before," Wyatt replied, "and I'm not starting now. Doc knocked Ike Clanton's gun out with a shot straight into his right wrist."

Wyatt Earp surveyed the scene. The bodies of the two MacLowerys and of Ike's son, Billy, were still oozing blood. The air smelt acrid with discharged powder. Morg and Doc were lifting up Virgil, carrying him between their two shoulders. Colonel Hooker strode into the yard at the front of the collected citizenry.

"Let me be the first man to shake you by the hand, Wyatt. That sure was fine shooting."

"Outlaws don't know how to shoot. They reckon that if they make enough noise they'll scare you." Wyatt started cleaning through the chambers of his Buntline Special. "Say, Doc!" he called, "where are you takin' Virg?"

"Back to the Cosmopolitan. It's only a light flesh wound."

"Oh, no, you're not!" Johnny Behan shouted from horseback, as he came riding into the corral. "You men are under arrest."

"What for?" growled Wyatt.

"Murder."

"*You* arrest *me*. The sky will have to turn green before I surrender to you, John Behan. I'm here willing to surrender to any duly authorized officer of the law, but I draw the line at handing over my gun to an outlaw Sheriff."

"You'll pay for this, Earp." Behan dug his spurs into his horse, wheeled her and rode out.

As Federal Deputy Marshal Wyatt was responsible for the safety of the mails and for serving Federal warrants and enforcing Federal orders, his duties did not extend to policing the town; that was the elected Sheriff's job.

Behan rode up to the courthouse where the Cochise County grand jury was sitting. Some of the Vigilantes had got there before him; already they were asking the jury to investigate the killings in the O.K. Corral. Behan pushed his way to the witness stand. He declared that the Clanton boys had been unarmed, that he had seen the Earp posse go in and shoot them down like dogs, and—what was more—he was the only eyewitness.

"Mister Sheriff," the jury foreman interrupted him. "We have evidence that Billy Clanton and his friends were going round town this morning swearing that they would kill the Earps. Why, come to that, I heard him myself."

"It isn't true," Behan answered back.

The roar of dissent from the rest of the jury and the crowd of Vigilantes in the well of the court showed Behan that he had lost that trick in the rubber. The grand jury found that the two MacLowerys and Billy Clanton had been killed by four peace officers in the execution of their duty.

Behan left court through the jeers of the Vigilantes. He went straightway across to Mosie Benton, Tombstone's one and only funeral undertaker. There he ordered the three finest caskets in stock; the three dead outlaws were to be lain in their caskets outside the parlour and over above Benton was to nail a placard reading "Murdered in the streets of Tombstone."

"Put the expense down to Cochise County," Behan remarked to the astonished undertaker, as he left in the same hurry as that in which he came in. The bell above the parlour door went on tinkling for a couple of minutes after he had left, so hard did he slam the door. Benton followed the Sheriff's course through the small glass slit in his otherwise black-draped window: the Sheriff had gone over to the *Nugget* office.

The next morning's issue of the *Nugget* appeared under banner headlines calling for the arrest of the Earps. Interviews with Johnny Behan, Billy Clanton and Billy Claiborne were published, each one giving a word-for-word account of how the Earps had surrounded five innocent cowboys on their way back to the ranch, and massacred them. And at precisely eleven o'clock Johnny Behan pushed through the swing-door of the courthouse as Judge Spicer was taking his seat. Within five minutes he came out of the building with four warrants for arrest stuffed in his pocket.

The news was soon over Tombstone. It reached Wyatt as he was steadying his cue for a cannon on the Cosmopolitan billiard table. "Don't interrupt a man when he's got one eye screwed!" he complained. Such was his tone of authority that nothing more was said until the fourth red ball had rolled into the pocket.

When he heard that Behan had sworn out warrants for murder, he slapped on his broad-brimmed Stetson and went over to Colonel Hooker's office. The advice that he got there was to go down to the courthouse and surrender to the Judge in person.

"All right, Colonel, if that's the way you want it," said Wyatt, and he went out of the door without saying another word. Back at the Cosmopolitan he collected Morg, Virg and Doc; the four of them then walked down to the courthouse.

Crowds gathered in Tombstone's courthouse like flies round a dead horse: somehow, some way whenever there was a murder charge to be tried every saloon emptied and every shop pulled down its shutters—there would be no more work done in Tombstone on that day.

When Judge Spicer was ready to hear the case against the three Earps and Doc, there was no room left in the court for a child of five. A sensation broke within a minute of the trial being called on: Johnny Behan demanded a twenty-four hour remand; his witnesses were not ready, he said. The Judge was prepared to grant the remand.

"How much bail do you want, Mr. Sheriff?" he asked Behan.

"No bail at all. These men are murderers. I demand they be handed over to me and be locked up for the night, your Honour."

There was a murmur of amazement in the crowd; most of them realized that the chances of the Earps surviving a night under Johnny Behan's care were about as great as the camel getting through the needle's eye. Judge Spicer had been in Tombstone long enough to sense the danger.

"I'm not doing that, Mr. Sheriff!" he said curtly.

"Then I'm asking for 50,000 dollars bail for each man." The Sheriff looked furious.

"That's big money, Mr. Sheriff," Judge Spicer answered, rapping the end of his pencil on the desk in front of him. "What precedent can you quote for such a sum being demanded?"

"What precedent is there for five innocent men to be shot down in a city street?"

There was a roar in the well of the court at this remark; it seemed as if fighting was going to break out between the Vigilantes and the Clanton supporters. Judge Spicer rapped his gavel fiercely. "I'm not here to answer questions, Mr. Sheriff. Application dismissed. Each man will stand remanded until eleven o'clock tomorrow morning in his own surety of 10,000 dollars. Court is adjourned!" The Judge got up out of his chair and marched from the room.

Next morning the *Nugget* came out with a front page that suspended all work in Tombstone. Close on five thousand gathered outside the courthouse, and when the usher opened the door it was like a whirlpool as the crowd eddied through the aperture into the building.

Judge Spicer summed up the situation. There would be no chance of holding a trial under these conditions; more likely the courthouse would be destroyed in the mêlée that was bound to break out between the two sides. With a sharp rap on the desk he announced that the court would be cleared except for the lawyers, the prisoners and the one witness on the stand. This decision caught Johnny Behan off-guard. The carefully concocted stories of the three witnesses had been written up by

Flames were roaring towards the wigwam

Harry Woods; when they got into the witness stand, they muffed the part and contradicted each other.

Judge Spicer was not impressed. Colonel Hooker, the Earp's attorney, rose to his feet. He started to open the case for the Defence. "You need not bother, Colonel," the Judge told him. "I'm dismissing the charges. The People have failed to make a case. Wyatt, Virgil, Morgan Earp and Doctor Holliday—you leave this court with a clean character."

Wyatt pushed his way out of the court building; there was a barrage of abuse from the Clanton boys when they saw what had happened. Johnny Behan came up to Earp and fairly spat in his face: "You may have got away with it here in Tombstone; but I am not finished with you yet. I'll swear out another warrant in Pima County."

"Swear as much as you please, Johnny, but don't try to serve the warrants yourself." Wyatt walked on without bothering. "I'll surrender to any other court in the United States you choose and lick the daylight out of your perjured evidence."

Behan was about to pull out his gun, when Ike Clanton got hold of his arm. "Let him alone, Johnny. Wise boy is going to learn the hard way."

Johnny Behan muttered something under his breath, and put the gun back into its holster.

Later that day Doc Holliday was careering down Fremont Street in search of some liquor: the only anaesthetic he gave his patients was a tumblerful of whisky. Just then he had run out of supplies; he had been celebrating his acquittal rather too copiously. Who should he bump into but Johnny Ringo right outside the Occidental Hotel. Johnny snarled.

"You sure look in a hurry, Doc. You and your friends decided to beat town at last?"

"I'm doing no such thing, you low-down jackanapes!"

"That's dangerous talk, Doctor." Ringo was fingering his gun. "No one's talking to me like that and getting away alive. Reach!"

"I haven't got my rod on me. But if I had . . ." Doc was plainly disappointed to be losing such a good opportunity.

"Then go back to that tooth cemetery of yours and fetch it. I'll wait for you here."

Doc forgot all about the patient strapped into his dentist's chair and the liquor he had gone out to fetch. The miserable patient with his tooth hanging half out of his jaw gave a great hollow of pain as he heard Doc running out of the door.

"Back soon, old-timer. Make yourself comfortable!" Doc shouted as he tripped down the doorsteps with his six-shooter in his hand. When he got back to the Occidental, Wyatt was standing there. The Marshal was having no nonsense.

"There ain't going to be no fight, Doc," he announced.

"Oh, so there ain't, ain't there," replied Doc, tossing his six-shooter in the air and catching it again.

"Put that gun back!" Wyatt rasped the command, and Doc recognizing the tone, slowly pushed the pistol back into the holster.

"It sure is a shame that a couple of gentlemen can't be having a discussion in this town," Doc complained. But Wyatt was not listening; he was beckoning to one of the new deputies he had just enrolled. The youngster was standing just behind Ringo. At the sign from Wyatt he seized the outlaw by the wrist of each arm and held him pinioned.

"Drop it, Ringo!" Wyatt barked.

Unwillingly the outlaw let his gun clatter on to the roadway.

"March him off to the calaboose!" Wyatt commanded.

"Now, why wouldn't you let me deal with him, Wyatt?" Doc inquired plaintively.

"Because—just in case you hadn't noticed—there was a rifle muzzle sticking out of the upstairs window of the Occidental. While you'd gone to fetch your gun Ringo had fixed it with one of the other Clanton boys. You'd have been a dead duck as soon as you had lifted your gun."

"Oh! If it's like that, Wyatt, what are we wasting time carting this louse off to clink for? Why don't we just take him out to where there is a nice strong tree and hoick him up?"

"Doc Holliday!" Wyatt tried to make his voice sound shocked: "I'd have you know that there is such a thing as law in this town and that you happen to be one of the officers of the peace."

"Quite right, Wyatt!" Doc was sounding subdued. "It's my imagination that gets the better of me."

Wyatt and Doc handed Ringo over to the man in charge of the calaboose; he was one of Behan's deputies. Within half an hour Johnny had been fetched out of a faro game to come and book in a prisoner. When the Sheriff looked into the cell and saw that the prisoner was none other than John Ringo, he unlocked the gate and led him into the office. Ostentatiously he put Ringo's gun on the table, the very gun that Wyatt had had taken off the outlaw, and then he turned his back on the prisoner.

"If you're here by the time I tie up the lace on my boot, Johnny," said the Sheriff, bending down to ground. But there was no need to say more: Johnny had picked up his gun and gone.

J. P. Clum brought out a triumphal edition of the *Epitaph* to celebrate the collapse of Behan's charges against the Earps and the formation of Tombstone's force of Vigilantes. "This marks the beginning of the end for Ike Clanton and his gang of cow-rustlers," was the way J.P. started his leading article, and each word was printed in the heaviest leaded type that could be found in the whole of Arizona.

"You're asking for trouble with this sheet of yours, J.P." Wyatt told him. "You don't think that the Clanton boys are going to sit still under that sort of writing."

"If they don't sit still, they'll be lying still for a good deal longer. The Vigilantes will take care of them."

Wyatt was by no means so sure. It had taken him ten years steady practice to learn how to handle his pistol the way he could. Half those years had been spent out on the prairie shooting buffalo for the railroad contractors. He had never shot less than twenty-five beasts a day during that period. After that sort of training he could hit most marks, including a dime thrown into the air or the side of a playing card at fifteen yards. But these Vigilantes were a raw crowd. The Clanton boys were gun-happy, not half as quick on the draw as their boasts would have their hangers-on believe, but for all that they could shoot straight. Wyatt did not give the Vigilantes one chance in ten if the Clanton boys rode into town in strength; but he did not tell J. P. Clum what he thought.

"All the same, J.P., I wouldn't sting 'em more than need be. You know how it is with wasps. The best thing is to leave 'em alone till you've got a rag to smother them." Wyatt gave the editor a friendly pat on the back before going out into the street towards the Cosmopolitan. He ordered himself a lime-juice when he reached the bar. As it happened, liquor did not agree with his inside. But the rest of the world did not know that; they reckoned that Wyatt's teetotalism was part of his austere character. The Clanton boys in particular used to poke fun at his abstemious habits; they called him "dog collar" behind his back. Wyatt knew all about the nickname; secretly he was rather amused; he liked the character build-up that his enemies gave him.

There was a crowd in the bar of the Grand Hotel, all of them trying to talk at once to Wyatt. The Marshal did not feel in the mood for discussion; he answered with "yes" and "no". But when Jack Altman, the desk clerk asked him whether he knew that Ringo, Curly Bill, Ike Clanton and a couple more had booked themselves rooms in the hotel, Wyatt found himself asking questions. "When had they come?" "Which way did the rooms face?" Jack Altman was rather vague in his answers. Wyatt's face looked troubled; he drained his glass and pushed out through the bat-wing doors.

Wyatt went round to look for his brothers. Both of them were hardened gamblers. The Earps were not in the peace officer business for the fun of it, but because Uncle Sam paid good money to those who lived dangerously. Even so, the money was nothing like enough for their dreamed project —buying up an established mine and hitting the jackpot. Sure enough, Wyatt tracked his brothers down to Joyce's Casino, where money changed hands so quickly that a man had to keep his wits or he would go home leaving an IOU for his next year's wages.

"D'you mind quitting the table, Morg?" Wyatt called across to his brother.

"Just let me play out this shake." Wyatt had to wait for a few minutes; he used the time to survey the faces round the gambling table. Everyone of them was taut with strain; as the dice rolled out on to the green baize, so a man's fortune was made or lost. "What a miserable lot!" Wyatt thought to himself. "Can't think why anyone should want to gamble unless he's desperate."

"Well, what is it?" His musing was interrupted by Morgan and Virgil coming up to him.

"Best come outside." Wyatt jerked his head towards the door.

Wyatt Earp goes into the Cosmopolitan

"Curly Bill and Ringo are in town with Ike Clanton and some of the other outlaws. I locked up Ringo once, but he's away. They've checked in at the Grand. I don't like it."

"What d'you reckon that we better do about it?" Virgil asked.

"Nothing except walk carefully, and get a pair of eyes to look out of the back of your head."

Within forty-eight hours Virgil had crumpled up on the sidewalk outside the Grand. A gun tip had been pushed through one of the shutter slats in an upstairs bedroom. By good grace Virgil had only been struck in the thigh, but the bullet had gone straight to the bone and splintered it. Coming on top of the flesh wound in the calf five days previously, the loss of blood proved very nearly fatal. Three of the Vigilantes got him up from the ground and carried him into his room in the Cosmopolitan. Someone ran to fetch Doc. He threw down his forceps into his Gladstone bag, scooped one or two more instruments in, gathered up a bottle of "anaesthetic" and left his surprised patient without so much as an excuse.

Wyatt was alarmed. The blood from Virgil's thigh was spilling everywhere. Unless Doc could stop it, Virg would go out like a candle. Doc saw the look of anxiety on Wyatt's face as he entered the room.

"There ain't no point your hanging around here, Wyatt," he said. "You go out and get your hands on those rats: I'll do what's necessary here."

Wyatt was relieved to have an excuse to do something; he was never at his ease when his hands were idle. He walked over to the *Epitaph* office to find out if J. P. Clum had heard the news. The report of the shooting had spread as fast as the echo of the shot. Clum was already scribbling out an article denouncing the men guilty of the cowardly attack. They discussed what to do about it. Clum wanted Wyatt to call out the Vigilantes and march on the Grand. Wyatt was dead against the plan. To start with, he explained, the outlaws would have ridden straight out of town; and even if they had not, there was a not a chance of driving them out of the top floor of the Grand before they could have picked off at least a dozen Vigilantes with their rifles.

"Well, what d'you aim at doing, Wyatt?"

"I've not rightly made up my mind yet. But there is one thing you could do to help, J.P. Wire to the Governor and ask him to expedite the Board of Elections' investigation into the Tombstone voting. Virgil ought to be Sheriff of this town, and he will be when the voting's checked. I'd kind of like him to have the badge on his chest soon in case he goes under. See if you can hurry it along, will you?"

"I certainly will." Clum picked up the pad of telegraph forms and wrote a message straightway. Wyatt went back to the hotel.

Doc was arranging the covers over Virg's shoulders, tucking him in, when Wyatt came. Morg told him that Doc was a wonder. He had got the lead out of the leg and tied the bone to a splint. Virgil was asleep; Doc had given him some pills. Doc smiled like a pleased child when the two brothers thanked him. "My job's easy," he said. "You've got the hard one. Someone has got to stay on guard in this room until Virg is fit enough to pick up a gun again."

"Yeah, I'd reckoned the same way myself," Wyatt answered. "Morg! I'll do the first two hours. Come back and give me a let-up when you've had a walk round town and bit of chow."

When Morgan returned, he came with a telegram for Wyatt, which Clum had handed to him. Wyatt snatched the envelope. His brow furrowed.

"What's wrong, Wy?"

"Just a message from over at Contention. Johnny Behan's sworn out murder warrants before a cowboy Justice of the Peace and deposited them at the courthouse there."

"You don't mean it!"

"He said he hadn't finished with us. And we haven't finished with him, Morg. If only we didn't have to sit here guarding Virg, we could go over right away and have something to say to that rascal."

The days passed by. Virgil was able to sit up in bed, but it was clear that it would be a long time before he could use his leg again. The State Board of Elections had upset the Tombstone voting and ordered a new poll. Virgil wanted to run for Sheriff again, but Wyatt had to advise him that it was hardly to be expected that the people would vote for a man in bed. So, the Law and Order Party found another candidate among Wyatt's deputies and started to make plans for the election.

Wyatt spent quite a while in consultation with Colonel

Hooker over the new warrants sworn out by Johnny Behan. Rumour had come that Behan had sworn Curly Bill, Ringo and Old Man Ike Clanton himself as deputies for the purpose of serving the warrants; it was a manœuvre to protect the outlaws from the Tombstone Vigilantes. Even in those days, when the verdict passed on most murderers was "self-defence", the courts took a serious view of killing a man with a deputy's badge. Rightly, Behan reckoned that the Vigilantes would think twice before firing on a Sheriff's posse.

Colonel Hooker advised Wyatt to send a message to Behan that he would not surrender to him or to the cowboy justice at Contention, but that he was ready and willing to present himself at the Contention Courthouse when the State Judge came round on circuit. Johnny Behan wired back accepting the offer, adding that Judge Horner would be reaching Contention in a week's time. Johnny was relying on the absence of the Tombstone Vigilantes to secure Earp a verdict of guilty at Contention.

Meanwhile Wyatt had fixed up with some of the Vigilantes to mount guard over Virgil. For the first time in over a fortnight he got the chance to go out with a Wells, Fargo coach. Not that the company was pressing him, because back at their San Francisco office they rated no one more valuable than Wyatt. He could have had any job he wanted any day. But, the truth was Wyatt was in need of the money. Virgil's illness had cost him most of his pile—it had meant sending for expensive medicines from 'Frisco.

Wyatt left Morg in charge of order in Tombstone. Now, Morg was a good shot and a fearless man, but he lacked the eye-twinkle that distinguished Wyatt from his other brothers. Consequently he found himself up against situations that he could only handle by shooting. He just about escaped with his life through Wyatt riding up at the last moment when everything seemed over. A bunch of drunk miners were reeling up Fremont Street on Saturday evening when they barged into the window of Altman's, the new jeweller's shop. The plate-glass window had splintered and, perhaps it was more than human nature could have expected, it was not many seconds before there was a wild rush to clear out the contents of the showcases. Morg was called to the scene by the frantic jeweller, who was running about the streets in his nightgown. At once the acting Marshal started issuing threats of what he would do if the men didn't back out of the shop. But the miners were too drunk with liquor and greed to hear what he was bawling. Instead of getting in after them and hauling them out by the scruff of the neck Morg raised his gun and fired into the shop. One of the miners let out the squeal of a dying pig, though truth to tell he had only been grazed. The men turned round, saw Morg with his six-shooter smoking, and then all hell was let loose.

Wyatt was riding up the street on his way to the Cosmopolitan after bringing in the Tuscon mail. With a quick glance his trained eyes summed up the situation. The men were charging towards Morgan, who was standing there with his gun poised ready to fire, but uncertain whether he dared blow six shots at point-blank range into a crowd of drunken sots. Wyatt leapt down from the saddle, went over to a water-butt standing under a drainpipe, heaved it up into the air and pitched the contents at the mob. It was a herculean feat; and it caught the miners off balance. The water served to sober up those it hit, and the rest burst out laughing at the discomfiture of their friends. Like with the passage of a magic wand the situation was changed, the tension vanished; Morgan could put away his gun.

It might have been guessed that Morgan would lose some friends and make some enemies during his term of office as Wyatt's deputy. But no one in his wildest imagination would have thought that his office would end the way it did.

It was like this: one evening—it was two days before the Earps were leaving for Contention—Wyatt had got in late from escorting the express. He was tired, so he declined Morg's invitation to go round and have a game of billiards.

"I think I'll go upstairs and put my head on the pillow, thanks, Morg," said Wyatt getting up from the meal.

"That's not like you, Wy. Sure you are all right?"

"Sure, I am."

"Guess you know best, Wy. I reckon I'll shuffle round to Jinks' and see if I can pick up a game in the saloon."

Up in the bedroom Wyatt sat down on the bed and pulled off one of his boots. That's better, he said to himself: I guess these boots of mine are getting a bit tight. He pulled off the other, stretched out his feet, and all of a moment or two felt ever so much fresher. He glanced at his watch; it was still quite early.

He decided that he would have a wash-down, change his kit and then have a stroll round to the billiard saloon.

Morg was in the middle of a break. The saloon crowd was standing around the table betting with each other how long Morg could keep it up.

"Hullo, Wyatt," one of them called as he noticed the Marshal enter. The others looked up and greeted him.

"Lay you sevens to threes that Morg will not reach a hundred," a punter suggested.

"I'll take that," cried Wyatt. "Make it in tens." He had good reason to put heavy money on his brother; he was as good a shot with a cue as he was with a gun.

"Stand back!" Morgan edged the crowd away with the tail-end of his cue. "Give a man a chance." The onlookers drew back, leaving Morgan a clear space at the end of the table. He leant forward, slid the cue slowly up and down his outstretched forefinger; and then—just as he had drawn back the cue to strike—there was a crack and a flash. The frosted glass window of the saloon collapsed in tinkling fragments. Morg clasped his hand to his heart, reeled and then collapsed over the table.

Wyatt turned towards the window and within the fraction of a second fired a deadly salvo from each of his guns. But it was dark outside, and the chance of hitting anyone was slim. A groan of pain betrayed that one of Wyatt's slugs had struck flesh; then there was the clatter of a half a dozen pairs of boots racing away down the street. Wyatt threw himself through the broken pane and started to run after the fugitives, firing from the hip. But they had the lead of him, and when his guns needed recharging, he called off the chase and trotted back to Jinks' to find out how Morg was.

His brother had been stretched out on top of the green table. "He's still breathing," one of the crowd hastened to assure Wyatt. "Best get him back to the Cosmop," Wyatt ordered. "If he's going to peg out, he might as well do it on his own bed." With a heave he slung the body of his unconscious brother over his back, and staggered towards the door.

Morg was past any attention that Doc could give. He came round for a few moments and nodded towards Wyatt. His elder brother leaned forward to catch the whisper of the mumbling lips. The sentence completed, Morgan's head dropped back on the pillow and his heart came to a full stop.

"What did he say?" Doc asked.

"That's between Morg and me." Wyatt's voice was gruff with anger. Doc flushed pink, as if he was in some way to blame. He stooped down to close the dead man's eyelids.

"I guess there's not much more we can do here," he said.

The next day Morgan Wyatt was buried in the cemetery field on the edge of the town. The dignity of the little graveyard had been brusquely disturbed only a few days before; someone had fancied that a vein of silver lay beneath the graves, so with scant courtesy had proceeded to throw up the coffins like slag on a heap. That was Tombstone all over. So was the style of the funeral; all the Vigilantes turned out to join the procession and a great many more besides. They filed after each other in a long line to throw a spadeful of earth on top of the coffin and then swarmed back to the Cosmopolitan. "Drinks on the house," had been Wyatt's order. For the rest of the day the mourners crowded round the bar counter, growing more and more maudlin.

"Poor ole Morg. He wash a goosh felleh!"

" 'Ave another one. Got to drink to Morg."

As soon as the last drunk had been propelled through the hotel doors Wyatt got round to acting on his plans. He went up to Virgil's room and sat down beside the bed.

"Virg, I'm going to shift you west to California. This is no place for a sick man."

"But, I don't want to quit now, Wy."

"Sure, I know that you're no quitter, but I'm going myself, Virg. I'm going to hand myself over to the Judge at Contention. I can't leave you here by yourself."

Virgil heaved a sigh. "What you says goes."

The next day Virgil was carried down to the waiting Wells, Fargo coach to be transported to Tucson and thence by rail to California. Riding beside the coach were Wyatt and Doc Holliday. It was dark by the time that they reached the railroad junction at Tucson. Doc and Wyatt carried Virgil into the car of the train. As he drew himself up, Wyatt cast a glance out of the window. Silhouetted against the moonlit sky were the figures of four men crouching on a flat car in a train drawn up on a siding. Instinctively Wyatt stepped back from the open window, edging himself into a protected position from which he could fire. After what seemed an age of waiting, but which was probably not more than five minutes, one of the shadows brought out a rifle from the truck. As he raised the gun to his shoulder Wyatt fired; the streak of flame spat through the darkness. The silhouettes disappeared. With a bound Wyatt was out of the car down on the track.

In the distance he could see figures running across the track; he fired again. The locomotive let out a snort of steam that temporarily blocked his vision; when it cleared, there were two or three men walking unconcernedly up the track. Were these the attackers? Wyatt rushed up to one, stared at his face, failed to recognize anyone that he knew. But the next man he knew all right; it was Frank Stilwell, one of the most notorious of the outlaws. Wyatt asked for no explanations; he shot him down before he could open his mouth. Leaning down to look at the face of his victim, Wyatt murmured: "That's one for Morg." The locomotive wailed into the night, summoned up its strength and drew out westwards carrying Virgil to safety.

Wyatt's determination to break up the Clanton gang was doubled by the cowardly plot to murder his wounded brother. As the Marshal rode along with Doc towards Contention, he said: "Mark my words, Doc. There's going to be no quarter from now on. It's them or us. If they don't keep to the rules of the game, nor do we."

"Now, that's talking the way I like to hear," Doc beamed cheerily and jollied along his horse.

Contention was in tumult by the time that they reached there. The Tombstone Vigilantes had rode in only an hour before; in that short space of time they had made it unmistakably clear to the citizens of Contention that Wyatt Earp was going to have a fair trial. So far as the burghers of Contention were concerned, that was quite all right; but Sheriff Behan had some very different ideas. When Johnny saw what was in the wind, he called his deputies together and told them that he was getting out of town—it was growing a deuced sight too hot.

"What about the charges against Earp?" Claiborne asked.

"The Judge'll just have to make out the best he can," replied Johnny.

When the court usher called on the case of the People of Arizona *v.* Earp and others, there was no answer from the prosecutor.

"What sort of a case is this?" asked the Judge.

"A framed-up case, your Honour," Colonel Hooker rose to explain.

"If that's the case, Colonel, it don't seem a very good frame. Are you asking me to dismiss the suit?"

"I most certainly am, your Honour."

"If Sheriff Behan hasn't the decency to prosecute his own charges, that's the least I can do. I dismiss the defendants Earp and Holliday with costs against the county."

For the second time in a fortnight Wyatt and Doc strolled out of a courthouse free men. The Vigilantes crowded round them, begging to be allowed to shake hands. Out came Colonel Hooker from the court.

"What are you waiting for, boys?" he roared. "Lift 'em up and chair 'em round town!"

One of the boys pulled out a cornet and another got hold of a drum. Up and down the main street they marched, singing "Glory, glory, Alleluia!" The citizenry of Contention stood by to let them pass, amazed.

"Let me down, for Jupiter's sake!" Wyatt implored. At last, they lowered him to the ground. Wyatt stormed up to Colonel Hooker.

"While your boys have been carting us round like circus monkeys Johnny Behan has been riding out into the scrub."

"Take it easy, Wyatt," interrupted the attorney, commander of the Vigilantes.

"I'm not takin' anything easy," Wyatt snapped. "Get Doc and me a couple of fresh horses instead of standing around here like gaping fools."

Two horses were led up. Wyatt vaulted into the saddle, and Doc followed suit. He spurred the animal, and she shot forward.

"Come on, boys," shouted the Colonel, catching the mood of impatience. "What are you waiting for?"

Within five minutes the troop of eighty Vigilantes were clattering down the main street, firing off into the air just to show Contention that they meant business.

Wyatt and Doc galloped towards Rourke's ranch. It was a

45

fair guess that some of the Clanton boys would be there, or at any rate Rourke would know which way they had gone. Wyatt dismounted in the ranch corral and strode up to the door. There was no one about, so he searched the rooms. Inside the kitchen there was Rourke stretched out in an arm-chair fast asleep. That's queer, thought Wyatt to himself. Rourke has many vices, but going to sleep in the middle of the afternoon isn't one of them. Wyatt turned about and went out again. Scarcely had he crossed the threshold into the corral when Rourke came running up behind him.

"You won't go away without having some chow, sure to goodness?" Rourke said coaxingly.

Wyatt turned to face him. "Sure to goodness," he said sarcastically, "I thought you were asleep."

"Must have just dropped off," the old rancher mumbled.

"Got any other sleepers here?" queried Wyatt.

"Only myself. The boys are all out on the range."

Wyatt looked him up and down. "We'll see about that. Show me into these stables!"

To start with, Rourke was quite obliging about unlocking doors, but when they came to a shed at the bottom of the corral, he drew up unsteadily. "You don't want to bother looking in there. That's where I keep a lot of old rubbish."

"Then I'd particularly like to have a look at your old rubbish, Mr. Rourke." Falteringly, the rancher unlatched the door. Wyatt stepped into the opening ahead of him. "Come on out with your hands up!" the Marshal commanded. There was a clatter at the back of the shed. Wyatt pointed his gun at the roof and fired. "Come on out, I said!" And out clambered a brace of dishevelled outlaws.

Wyatt drove them into the yard at the end of his pistol.

"Where's Behan gone?" he thundered.

There was no reply. The two men stared at the ground.

"Are you going to talk? Or is my six-shooter going to do the talking?" Wyatt tossed his gun into the air, caught it and pointed it at them just to emphasize his point.

Again there was no reply.

"Very well. Mr. Rourke, will you do me the favour of fetching me a spade out of the place where you keep your old rubbish?"

"What's the idea?" inquired Doc.

*Wyatt, Doc, Colonel Hooker and the rest of the Vigilantes
galloped off towards Deadman's Gulch*

47

"These two gentlemen are going to have the pleasure of digging their own graves before I shoot 'em," Wyatt answered with the bitterness hissing in his voice.

The outlaws looked at each other in terror.

"You win," said the tall one, "we'll talk."

"Talk quick!" ordered Wyatt.

"Ike Clanton was here waiting for Behan," the outlaw spoke fast as if his life depended on his finishing the sentence without taking a breath. "As soon as Behan came in from Contention the whole gang rode off to Deadman's Gulch; we were left behind to rake up the news and carry it back to the others."

Wyatt looked at the outlaws with faint disgust. Then he turned to glance over the corral stockade, to where a cloud of dust was rising over the scrub.

"That'll be the Vigilantes," he said to Doc. "We'll detail a half-dozen of those boys to ride the three of them back into Tombstone."

"No, you don't get me like that!" Rourke whipped his gun out.

"Put that down!" roared Wyatt, and as he spoke Rourke's hand fell limp to his side with a bullet straight through it. "Now, get over there." He jerked him over towards the other two outlaws at the end of his gun.

As soon as the necessary instructions had been given, Wyatt, Doc, Colonel Hooker and the rest of the Vigilantes galloped off towards Deadman's Gulch. After a short night's rest they came on a water-hole early the next morning. As they approached, they could see three or four bodies lying on the ground, asleep. The thump of hooves wakened them up, but too late. Wyatt was riding full tilt at them, firing as he raced. They had no time to reach for their guns. Two dropped down dead. The other two thought better of making a fight; they dashed to their horses and made off.

The Vigilantes spurred their horses to make chase. "Whoa!" shouted Wyatt. The men turned to look over their shoulders: Wyatt was waving them back.

"What's up?" they wanted to know.

"Give 'em a bit of leeway, and they'll lead you to the rest of the gang," Wyatt replied.

Doc came up to report: "That's none other than Curly Bill himself with a couple of your bullets through his chest."

"Who's the other one?" queried Wyatt, unmoved.

"Don't recognize him, but Colonel Hooker says that he's one of the gang's contact men."

"Good," said Wyatt. "That's another two for Morg! Send a couple of men back to Tombstone with the news. Have J.P. splash Curly Bill's death all over the *Epitaph*."

"Sure will, Wyatt." Doc hurried off to carry out the instructions.

The chase continued. The two escaping outlaws lead them up mountainside and down into sandy valley, across waterless wastes and through horse-high reed-grass. But they never caught up with the rest of the gang. After a day of it, Wyatt grew exasperated.

"It's no use following much farther. Either these guys are acting dumb or else they are dumb."

"How do you mean?" Doc inquired.

"Either they're heading us away from Clanton and Behan, or else they've lost the track themselves."

"What do you reckon to do then?"

"Haul 'em in now. Come on, let's go!" Wyatt let out his horse to a full gallop. He streaked across the plain. Within ten minutes he had made up the difference between the posse and the two outlaws. If they had intended to make a fight, they had no chance to try. Wyatt shot down their horses under them, and rounded them up like a couple of stray buffaloes.

The following evening the posse rode into Tombstone with its two prisoners. The inhabitants came out on to their doorsteps; J. P. Clum was standing outside the Cosmopolitan. Wyatt reined in his horse to speak to him.

"Get the message, J.P.?"

"Sure did, Wyatt. Went to town on it."

"What's the *Nugget* say about that?"

"Came out with an offer to give fifty dollars to anyone who could prove that Curly Bill wasn't still alive."

"That's fifty dollars that I'll be pleased to collect right now."

Wyatt stormed into the *Nugget* office. "Who's there?" he called out. There was no reply. The office showed every sign of having been hastily abandoned. The drawers were pulled out, the cupboards open; papers littered the floor. "Mighty odd," Wyatt said aloud. "Hm! What's this?" He went over to look at a piece of paper nailed on to the wall with a Bowie knife. Scrawled across it were the words: "Closed. Forward mail to Mexico City."

"So that's the end of the Clanton gang," Wyatt said to anyone who might be there to listen. "Crossed the border!"

"D'you aim to follow them, Wyatt?" J.P. was standing beside him.

Wyatt kicked at the litter of paper by his feet. "Nope! Three for one's a good enough score. The rest of the galuts can go hang themselves so long as they never show up in Arizona no more."

"What do you know?" Doc clapped his hands. "If you were to ask me, this occasion calls for a little celebration."

"For once you're right, Doc." Clum patted him on the back. "But you'll have to excuse me; I've got to get out a special edition of the *Epitaph*."

Back at his desk J. P. Clum licked the point of his pencil. He had written: "*A chapter has closed. The clouds have gone. The night is past. The rule of the gun in Tombstone is ended. From henceforth to the end of time a woman can walk safely to the end of the street, a man can hang his six-shooter up on the wall. A new day has dawned. . . .*"

John Clum scratched his head. "It is going to be kind of dull round here," he thought to himself.

THE RIDE TO KANSAS

All was quiet in Kit Carson's lonely little camp pitched high on a hill in New Mexico.

No one was in the camp except Oompa: and Oompa's eyes were searching the far horizon (as they had been doing for many days past) for any sign of the approaching return of Kit and Pico. But nothing stirred in the desolate waste of sand and rock; and Oompa sadly concluded that today's dinner (like all the other dinners that he had prepared for them every day since they had left) would once again go uneaten.

Oompa was a very small and very fat Eskimo, and many years ago (far away in the north of America) had one day fallen into a treacherous ice-crevasse. His leg had been broken by the fall. For how many days and nights he had lain in the crevasse alone and incapable of movement, Oompa no longer remembered or wished to remember. But, one day, just as he had begun to think that help would never come, a strange voice had shouted to him and a strange face had looked down on him.

Oompa remembered little more of that day except that someone had hauled him out of the crevasse and had carried him for miles across the frozen ice. That someone had been Kit, who had then patiently nursed Oompa back to health, except for the very bad limp that now prevented Oompa from either riding, or even walking, very far. From then on, Oompa had attached himself to Kit—as friend, admirer and, above all, cook: for the thing that Oompa loved doing best of all in life was cooking.

Kit enjoyed Oompa's cooking; and so did Pico, the great, gaunt Indian who on one grey morning, also many years ago, had ridden into Kit's then camp.

Oompa still remembered that morning.

There had been a sudden great clatter of hooves approaching the camp. Looking out, Oompa had seen the Indian and Kit ride to the door of the tent and dismount; and, to his horror, had also seen that both were covered with blood, both wounded,

and Kit so severely wounded that he was practically unconscious. Oompa had at first been very suspicious of the tall,
gaunt Indian; and, small as he was, had tried to bar the Indian's
way into the tent. But he had found himself suddenly (and,
though very gently, also very firmly) being picked up by the
scruff of the neck and deposited in the far corner of the tent,
where, with absorbed eyes, he had watched the Indian tenderly
bathe Kit's wounds, apply some strange ointments to them and
then bind them up with pieces of cloth torn from the Indian's
shirt. When the Indian had finished, he had straightened up,
wiped the blood from his own face and, with something on his
lips that looked like a smile, had grunted to Oompa: "Me his
friend. Him my friend. You friend too?" A thoroughly
satisfied Oompa had chuckled back: "Me friend too. Cook
nice dinner for Boss." And from that day Pico and he had
been the firmest of friends. They talked to each other in some
strange language of their own that no one else could understand,
because, while Pico knew the English language quite well,
Oompa's English was confined to a few phrases of which his
favourite was the one already mentioned: "Cook nice dinner for
Boss."

It had only been weeks afterwards, when Kit had begun to
recover from his wounds and could explain things slowly to
Oompa (because Pico himself had never mentioned a word of
what had happened), that Oompa heard the story of that dreadful night.

Kit had been riding along a desert track in the then completely
wild country of Arizona whose only inhabitants at that time were
Indians of different and warring tribes whom the white man's
advance into the Great Continent had been slowly and relentlessly driving farther and farther west. Kit had suddenly heard
the yelling and whooping of Indian braves on the war-path; and
had seen a small party of Indians (no more than twenty in all,
men, women and children) being attacked by some two hundred
Indians of a different tribe. The small party was defending itself
as best as it could, but the odds had been too uneven and most
of them were already dead or dying and their camp was ablaze.

Kit had ridden through the attackers, firing simultaneously
with both of his guns, and had dispersed them but had himself
been badly wounded by their answering fire and had fallen from

his horse. As the attackers had ridden off, one of them had seen Kit lying in the sand, had swiftly dismounted and was about to scalp him. But before the tomahawk could reach the helpless Kit's head, the Indian had crumpled up with a bullet through his heart, and Kit had seen, standing over him, the figure of Pico. Pico had put Kit back on Kit's horse and had said: "Ride with me. Nothing left here." Kit had looked round. It was quite true. Apart from Pico himself, all the rest of the little party were dead. Pico had pointed to one body. "My squaw," he had said. And then to another. "My papoose," he had said.

That had been the story that Oompa had heard; and it had made Pico, in his eyes, almost as much of a hero as Kit himself.

But a day had come when, with Kit nearly completely recovered, Pico had stood over Kit and had said: "I go now."

Oompa did not want Pico to go. Neither did Kit.

"Why?" said Kit.

"I go look for that Indian rat who . . ."

"I know," had interrupted Kit. "But tell me, Pico, who were these Indians who attacked you? You're a Black Hawk, aren't you?"

"Yes," had said Pico proudly. Kit had reflected. Even in these distant days he was already beginning to acquire that knowledge of the various Indian tribes that was later to make him one of the greatest experts in Indian life that America had ever known.

"But I didn't recognize *them*," he had said. "What tribe were they?"

"No tribe," had answered Pico scornfully. "Just scum. Sweepings of all the tribes—rats thrown out of all the tribes— robbers, thieves, murderers—led by the biggest rat that our Indian race has ever produced. I kill him, Kit, when I find him; and I go to search for him now."

"Where will you look for him?"

"I do not know—anywhere—everywhere."

"Why not stay with me? I go anywhere—everywhere. Let's try to find him together. You see, I too have a debt to pay off to that gentleman, though a much smaller debt than yours."

Pico had hesitated.

"Stay here," had said Kit firmly.

Oompa had chuckled delightedly. "Stay here" was a new

English phrase to him, and he liked the sound of it. "Stay here, stay here. Cook nice dinner."

Pico had suddenly bowed and answered: "I stay here."

CHAPTER II

Oompa's eyes were still searching the horizon, and they had just noticed a small speck in the sand about a mile away.

Oompa watched carefully. The speck became larger, and Oompa saw that it was a man, dragging his tired feet as he doggedly ploughed through the sand.

"If it's that Jake Bloom . . ." thought Oompa to himself. But no one will ever know what else Oompa would have thought or said because the man was now clearly in view and was not Jake Bloom at all. He was a young and handsome man whom Oompa had never seen before and was wearing clothes of a sort that Oompa had also never seen before. But Oompa liked his young, keen face and ran out to meet him and to help him into the tent.

"Thanks, pal," said the young man. "Does Kit Carson live here?"

"Kit Carson, yes," chuckled Oompa. "Boss like nice dinner, please."

"Who are you?" said the young man.

"Oompa," said Oompa.

"Okay, Oompa. Let's see that nice dinner, and let's see it quick!"

The young man saw it very quickly; and as he ate it ravenously, his eyes kept darting round the small tent.

"Where's Kit?" he asked several times. But Oompa never replied. He had been looking out of the tent during all the time that the guest had been eating, but as the young man, having finished his meal, asked once more "Where's Kit?" Oompa turned round with a great smile on his face and said "Here."

Round the corner of the little hill to the east of the camp, Kit and Pico were, in fact, coming, and in a few minutes they were both inside the tent.

"Nice dinner," shouted the overjoyed Oompa, as he bustled off.

"And who are you, sir?" said Kit, looking pleasantly at the young man. "Has Oompa entertained you well?"

"Very well, indeed, sir," said the young man, equally pleasantly. "I presume I'm addressing Mr. Kit Carson?"

"You are," said Kit.

"Well, then, this is for you."

He handed to Kit a letter sealed with a great red seal.

Kit opened the letter and carefully read it.

"I see," he said as he put it into his pocket.

His level eyes scrutinized the young man.

"Would *you* know, Lieutenant, what's in that letter?"

"I wouldn't *know*," was the answer, "but I *could* guess."

"Guess then."

"If the Pueblo Indians are on our side, we win this war."

"Why?"

"Because General Grant can then spare—*for other purposes*—the five thousand men who at the moment are being wasted on patrolling this territory." He paused.

"And?"

"And there's only one man who can get these Indians on our side; and I think that letter tells that man to do so.

"There is, Mr. Carson," he added, "going to be a big push—we in the army know that—by the Confederates within the next two months. These five thousand men would be a great help when that push does begin. But we must be sure, before we withdraw our men, that the Indians *will* be on our side."

His eyes twinkled mischievously as he glanced at Kit.

"Are you going to get that treaty, sir?"

Kit smiled back.

"I am, son. But you must keep your mouth shut about this."

"Do you think, sir," said the young man steadily, "that I *would* do otherwise?"

"I don't," said Kit, "but look here," he added suddenly. "It's just occurred to me that I don't even know your name. What is it?"

"Lieutenant Frank Goddard, Captain Christopher Carson."

Kit stared at him in amazement. The Lieutenant grinned.

"You see, sir, I've further orders. These orders are to come back here in four days' time and see if a certain person has a certain document. If that document is here I have then to tell the person who has it that he's a captain in the Union Army and must take the document at once to General Grant. Will the document be here?"

"You are, Lieutenant, both the most intelligent"—Kit started to laugh—"and the most cheeky young man I've ever met. The document will be here."

"When are you going, sir?" asked Goddard gravely.

"Now," said Kit.

"Dinner for Boss," said Oompa as he suddenly appeared with it.

Kit ate it hurriedly.

"Pico," he called. "We ride again—and at once."

"Where?" said Pico.

"Chief Great Antelope."

Pico's eyes gleamed.

"Chief Great Antelope good chief. Will do what Boss wants."

"And how," said the Lieutenant, "would you know what Boss wants?"

The two men looked at each other. The Lieutenant had liked Pico on sight, and it seemed as if the same had happened to Pico because he actually half-smiled as he grunted: "Maybe I hear what you say to Boss."

"Lieutenant," said Kit, rising, "there's no time to lose. I *will* be back here in four days' time."

"Back, Oompa," said Kit, holding up four fingers, "four days."

"Come, Lieutenant," he added, "you can go on the back of my horse: and I'll drop you off at the Fort."

Oompa looked as if he were about to burst into tears. They were always riding away and leaving him behind. He knew he couldn't ride these long distances but . . .

The Lieutenant chucked him under the chin.

"Cheer up, pal. Me back too. Four days. Nice dinner or . . ."

Oompa began to smile but suddenly darted to Pico and whispered something to him. Pico's face darkened.

"Boss," he said, "I do not ride. You are safe with Great Antelope and do not need me. I wait here."

"Why?" said Kit.

The Indian folded his arms and said impassively: "Oompa has news for me."

Kit studied Pico's face intently.

"Very well," he said shortly as he began to ride off.

"And what in the devil's name did all that mean?" asked the bewildered Lieutenant.

"I don't know," answered Kit slowly. "Pico sometimes acts queerly, but never," he added, "without some good reason."

He dropped the Lieutenant off at the Fort: and then rode as fast as he could to Great Antelope's camp.

CHAPTER III

Four days later Kit arrived back. The Lieutenant, Pico and Oompa were all waiting for him.

"Had your dinners yet?" growled Kit.

"Dinner's all ready," laughed the Lieutenant, "but we decided to wait for you. Get cracking, Oompa."

Oompa squealed with delight. "Get cracking" was another new phrase and he liked it. He scuttled off.

"All well with Great Antelope?" asked Pico. There was something like a smile on his face.

"Very, very well, Pico."

"Then I go to help Oompa." He left the tent.

"I like that fellow, Kit," said the Lieutenant. "He's guessed we want a minute or two together." He bent forward. "Tell me," he said eagerly, "what happened: and have you got it?"

"Of course I've got it," answered Kit sharply. "Here it is." He pulled out a roll of buffalo hide.

"Any difficulties?"

"None. Great Antelope is a grand chap. When I told him what I wanted he immediately agreed on behalf of his own tribe, and at once summoned the three chiefs of the other tribes for a grand palaver. The palaver lasted," said Kit rather ruefully, "all night; and I had to drink steadily to keep pace with the chiefs—which hasn't done my liver any good. But Yellow Eagle was on Antelope's side from the start. Brown Owl wavered a bit but soon agreed. The only really difficult customer was Caraba, the Chief of the Arakas. He's a nice fellow, really, but he's getting a bit old, and he kept on humming and hawing till even Antelope got impatient and began to try some peaceful persuasion with him."

"Peaceful persuasion?" laughed the Lieutenant. "What sort of peaceful persuasion?"

"You'd have loved it, son, if you'd been there," laughed Kit in reply. "Honestly, I've never seen anything like it in all my life. Antelope just picked up Caraba's gin, took it to a far corner of the room and said 'No signature, no gin.' Caraba signed, got his gin back, and all the signatures are there. Look."

The Lieutenant looked.

"Good for you, sir, but, for God's sake, do be careful with that roll. Put it away; someone's coming."

Someone was coming.

Jake Bloom came into the tent. He was a little wizened wiry man with shrewd and penetrating eyes that immediately fixed themselves on the Lieutenant with an inquiring look.

"Lieutenant Goddard, Jake Bloom." Kit made the introductions. "Jake, Lieutenant is a very old friend of mine and the best prospector in the whole of New Mexico."

"Proud to meet you, Lieutenant," said Jake.

"But where the devil, Kit, have you been this last fortnight or so?"

"Riding round," said Kit airily.

Jake's keen appraising eyes were still on the Lieutenant.

"I know," he drawled, "that you were up near that old tin mine for some days. What were you looking for?"

"Oil," answered Kit promptly. "And, Jake, I don't mind telling you that I think there is oil there."

"You do?" said Jake eagerly. He had taken his eyes off the Lieutenant, and there was a slight flush on his face.

"You know, Kit, I always thought that there might be, but I could never spot the exact place. If you've got it, well, our fortunes are made."

"I'm not guaranteeing anything," Kit began to say, when Oompa scuttled into the tent with two steaming hot plates, one of which he put before Kit and the other before the Lieutenant.

"Get cracking," he chuckled.

Jake threw a covetous glance at the plates. "That smells good to me. Could I have some, Kit? I'm feeling pretty peckish myself."

"Of course," said Kit. "Oompa, bring one for Jake."

The little Eskimo said in a curiously flat voice: "None left."

"Rubbish, Oompa. Bring some for Jake."

"None left," repeated Oompa with a very stubborn expression on his face.

Jake suddenly exploded.

"Do what you're told, you blasted Eskimo," he shouted, and, turning to Kit, said: "That fellow, Kit, is getting a side too impudent, and why you put up with him I don't know."

"Now, now," said Kit. "You know, Jake, you are always. misjudging Oompa. The poor chap is not mentally very bright, but he's a good fellow at heart. He'll soon cook more. Oompa, dinner for Jake."

Oompa stood stockstill and for the third time repeated: "None left."

Kit was embarrassed. So was the Lieutenant, and Jake was about to say something angry when Pico walked quietly into the tent and placed a plate before Jake.

"Come, Oompa," he said, but with such a curious inflexion in his voice that Oompa at once scuttled out of the tent like a shot rabbit.

Pico stood quietly and watched the three men as they ate. Little was said. All three were hungry. But, as Jake ate, his good temper slowly returned. "Sorry, Kit," he said, "but that idiot does get on my nerves at times, and you're much too easy with him."

"Maybe," grunted Kit through a large and savoury mouthful, "but he's my servant, Jake, and not yours."

"Okay, okay, old soft heart," laughed Jake. "Tell me more about the oil."

Kit had finished eating. "I've told you all there is to tell. I *do* think that oil *is* there, but we can both make sure later. By the way," he said, "how did you know I had been there?"

"One of my runners saw you heading that way," said Jake simply, "and I always put two and two together." He lit his pipe and grinned.

Kit grinned back.

"You're an old fox, Jake, and you don't miss much, do you?"

"Not much," agreed Jake, "and I haven't missed the fact either that this Lieutenant of the Union Army is here in your tent. But I think I can . . ." He paused as he drew on his pipe.

"Can what?" said Kit sharply.

"Figure out what he's doing here."

Kit threw him a very hard glance.

"Go on, figure."

"I'll figure," said Jake mildly, "if you'll tell me whether I'm right or wrong."

"Go on," said Kit.

Jake's pipe was going well as he leaned back in his chair and said:

"When you got back from that mine, you went off again somewhere else, and I don't know where. That's one thing I don't *know*." He was speaking in a very calm and steady voice. "But I find an army Lieutenant here when you do come back; and, as the Confederates are massing troops all along the border——"

"How do you know that?" interrupted the Lieutenant.

"Seen 'em," was the laconic answer. "Hundreds of 'em. Trickling along the border in small groups of twenties and thirties. And, although I'm no military man, seeming to me to be going to take up arranged positions for——"

It was Kit this time who interrupted.

"For what?"

"I would guess some kind of attack on the South-western Territories."

The Lieutenant swore savagely under his breath. Kit said quietly: "And what earthly good, Jake, would that do? The war won't be won down here."

"But it can be *lost* down here," was the significant answer. "A surprise attack. If it's successful then the tribes come out for the south. And then one-half of General Grant's army is stuck here, while the other half is being massacred some place else. Am I right, Lieutenant?"

The Lieutenant said nothing, but his face was very white.

"Go on, Jake," prompted Kit gently.

"Right so far?" asked Jake quizzically.

"Right so far. Go on."

"Well, if I *am* right so far, the rest is easy. The tribes *must not come out for the south. Somebody must stop them from doing so. Somebody must get them to agree not to do so*. There is only one person who could do that. That person has been away for some days, and an army officer is waiting for him on his return.

Did you or did you not, Kit," he rapped out suddenly, "go to the tribes?"

"There's no use fencing with you, Jake. I did," answered Kit, "and I've got a treaty in my pocket right here and now."

"A treaty?" breathed Jake. "Good for you. You called me an old fox just now. But you're a pretty smart old fox yourself, aren't you?"

Kit laughed.

"And the treaty goes to General Grant?"

"It does."

"And would you know where General Grant is?"

"I do," said the Lieutenant shortly. His voice was suspicious and rather hostile. "I'll tell him when you've gone."

"Quite right," said Jake approvingly. "A military secret is a military secret. But there's no need to tell him when I've gone." He wagged his pipe at the Lieutenant. "General Grant is in Kansas City. Got there a week ago."

"How the hell do you know?" swore the Lieutenant.

"Saw him arrive," said Jake laconically.

"Jake gets around," said Kit. "Never known a fellow get around like him." There was a curious quizzical expression on his face as he asked. "But is Kansas City the right answer?"

"It is," said the Lieutenant.

"And when that treaty gets to Kansas City," said Jake, "it will be worth at least a million dollars to the Union—or to anybody else."

"Or," interrupted Kit, very sharply, "some thousands of lives."

Jake turned to the Lieutenant and smiled.

"Old soft-heart here thinks more of lives than of dollars. But the only life he never thinks of is his own."

"And what," said Kit very, very sharply indeed, "would you mean by that, Jake?"

"How," rapped Jake, equally sharply, "are you going to get that treaty safely to Kansas City?"

"Just take it there," said Kit coldly, "and hand it over. Now what in hell, Jake, are you really getting at?"

Jake drew on his pipe.

"The river's in flood."

"Is it?" gasped the Lieutenant. "Then there are the——"

61

"Swamps," said Jake crisply. He looked at Kit.

"When the river's not in flood, Captain," said the Lieutenant, "the swamps on each side of it are very easy to pass. But once the river is in flood, these swamps are a sheer death-trap. I know. I've tried it. Are you sure," he said fiercely to Jake, "that the river *is* in flood? We've heard nothing yet at the Fort."

"Maybe," said Jake, "nobody at the Fort has been near that river since Tuesday. But I have, and it started flooding on Wednesday. I saw the start and nearly got caught in those damned swamps myself before I got through."

The Lieutenant swore savagely.

"Captain," he said. "This is going to make your job very much more difficult than I had thought. I know where to get through these swamps even when the river is in flood. But the Fort can't spare a single man—not even me—to assist you. How in hell you're going to get through them alone I just don't know."

Kit was nettled.

"Now look here, youngster, I was getting through swamps before you were even born. I'll get through these swamps too, and I won't be alone, anyway. Pico goes with me, don't you Pico?"

"As Boss says," answered Pico

Jake smiled sardonically. "Well, that's all right. Kit and Pico know nothing of these swamps. Do you, Pico?" Pico said nothing. "But *they*, Lieutenant, will just get through them. Just like that." He lit a match and blew it out. "Just like that," he repeated.

The Lieutenant jumped to his feet. He had forgotten all about Kit's new rank as he shouted out: "This is utter nonsense, Kit. If you don't know these swamps, you will never get through. Your lives are your own and you can risk them as and when you like. But that treaty means other people's lives, and its that treaty that must get through—not Pico nor even you." He was trembling with agitation.

"Quiet, son," said Kit very sternly.

"It's no use telling me to be quiet," snapped the Lieutenant angrily. "Either you know how to get through these swamps or you don't. If you don't, say so."

"You are extremely insolent, young man," said Kit with a very hard ring in his voice. "This is my job, not yours, so please sit down."

His face was very, very angry indeed as he added:

"I don't want any puppies to teach me my business."

Under this insult the Lieutenant's own face went white. He was about to say something but Jake rapidly intervened.

"Am *I* a puppy, Kit? Control that blasted temper of yours. The lad's just trying to help. No need to snarl at him. He asked you a question, and I'm going to ask you just the same question. So snarl at me now if you like."

Kit was already repenting of his outburst of bad temper.

"Go on," he said sourly.

"Do you or don't you," said Jake softly, "know how to get through these swamps?"

Kit hesitated.

"Or are you," said Jake relentlessly, "building yourself up in your own mind as the great hero who got stuck in the swamps, lost his life for his country in his valiant battle to get through and"—he jabbed suddenly towards Kit with the end of his pipe—"lost the treaty too?"

Kit was a rather bad-tempered man, and knew it and regretted it. He had already lost his temper once during the conversation, but Jake's new attack on him was too much, and he lost his temper for the second time.

"And are *you* going to teach me my business too?" he shouted with a face that was suffused with anger.

"I am," said Jake placidly, "and just listen to what I have to say. And, by the way," he added, "I'd like you to send Pico out for a moment."

"Why?"

"Kit please just do as I ask."

Kit's temper had subsided again.

"Okay. Pico, just go out for a minute."

"Pico go," answered the Indian as he obediently left the tent.

"Now," said Jake, comfortably drawing on his pipe, "we're all settled for a nice cosy chat. Do you or don't you know these swamps, Kit?"

"Do you, sir?" said the Lieutenant.

Kit looked at the two faces.

"I don't," he said shortly.

"That's better," said Jake. "Now we know where we are. And don't start flying into any more tempers. You've a big job on and you need all the help you can get. Sorry I spoke a bit roughly to you a minute ago." He patted Kit's arm affectionately. "But that's an old friend's privilege."

"Sorry I spoke roughly to both of you," said Kit rather shamefacedly, "but, Jake, your news of these swamps *did* worry me." He glanced closely at Jake. "Have you any suggestions, you old fox?"

"Well, I have," answered Jake, slowly removing his pipe from his mouth, "but the best one won't work."

"And what's that one?"

"To take this 'puppy' "—the Lieutenant blushed at the kind smile that accompanied the word—"with you. But you can't do that, son, can you?"

"Just can't. Not a single man, as I have already told you, can be spared from the Fort—not at least until this treaty does get to Kansas City."

Kit looked levelly at Jake.

"Well, that's your best suggestion. What's your next best?"

"Not a puppy this time, but a very old and shaggy fox. Me."

"But you nearly got drowned in these swamps yourself. You've just said so," protested Kit. "How can *you* get me through them?"

"Kit, I alone just can't, but I know a man who *can*. That man owes me a big debt of gratitude for something I did for him recently. He knows every inch of these swamps like the back of his hand. And, if I ask him, he'll take you through them."

"And who is he?" asked Kit suspiciously.

"That is why I wanted you," answered Jake carefully, "to send Pico out. This man's an Indian."

"Not by any chance," asked Kit, "one of that strange tribe that moved into the river basin some months ago?"

His eyes were very steady. Jake's were equally steady as he answered: "Indeed he is. He's their Chief, Big Red Eagle himself."

"I don't like the sound of this," said Kit very sharply. "That tribe is, so far as I know, not a real tribe at all. None of the

John Marsh hoists the White Bear flag

Indians hereabouts have ever heard of them, and neither have I. Can your Chief be trusted?"

"Absolutely," said Jake. "Absolutely," he repeated very firmly. "The Indians here wouldn't know his tribe naturally, because the tribe has just migrated down here from Colorado."

"But I still don't know them," said Kit rather angrily, "and I *did* think I knew every tribe in Colorado that mattered."

"Look, Kit," said Jake, "this job's getting on your nerves a bit. I've never known you to be so jumpy and suspicious in all your life before. If I say that this Chief *can* be trusted, isn't that good enough for you?"

Kit growled.

"Maybe the job *is* getting a little on my nerves, but the less people who know about it—unless they are absolutely trustworthy—the better."

Jake rose.

"Okay," he said very sharply, "then do it yourself." He walked to the door of the tent.

"Come back, you fool," shouted Kit. "What in hell are you playing at now?"

"It's either trust, Kit," said Jake sorrowfully, "or no trust. If you trust *me*, you will trust this Chief. If you don't trust me, you won't trust the Chief. That's all. Just please yourself."

He waited while Kit reflected.

"Why," said Kit suddenly, "had Pico to be out of the room while we were talking about this?"

Jake hesitated, but then said very deliberately and slowly: "Pico did not go to the chiefs with you, did he? Why not? And where, Kit, did he go during your absence? Do you know?"

To this rain of questions Kit gave no answer except to say, "Go on."

"Pico," said Jake, "is a Black Hawk. *You* trust Black Hawks, but I myself just don't."

"Pico's all right," said the Lieutenant suddenly.

"Maybe *he* is," was Jake's grim answer. "But, by and large, the Black Hawks are the dirtiest and most dangerous and most treacherous Indian tribe in the whole of America. Am I right, Kit?"

Kit answered, choosing his words very carefully: "I don't agree as regards the tribe in general, but it is true that there *have* been some very bad Black Hawks just the same as there have been some very bad Sioux, Algonquins, Arakas and all the rest."

"Then what," said Jake suddenly, "was Pico doing yesterday at the river's only fordable creek?"

"Was he there?" said Kit.

"He was. I saw him myself."

"You seem to see everything," growled Kit. "Troops massing one day, General Grant at Kansas City another day, Pico at the creek still another day."

"And all true," said Jake simply. He drew steadily on his pipe.

"All true, Kit," he repeated. "Call me a liar if you like, but *it's all true. Every single word.*"

Kit sat back. His eyes were very suspicious, but he knew that everything that Jake had told him must have been completely and literally true.

"Very well," he said abruptly, "what do you actually suggest?"

Jake replied equally abruptly: "Meet me at the Rock tomorrow morning at 8 a.m. I'll send my Indian runner on in advance to White Falls tonight. When you and I get there, the Chief will be waiting for us. He'll guide us through the swamps. Then a night's rest at his camp on the other side, and then off you yourself go to Kansas City. Fair enough?"

"Fair enough," said Kit. He looked inquiringly at the Lieutenant.

"Fair enough," said the Lieutenant. "But I only wish that I could be there, too."

"Let's go then," said Jake. "Coming, Lieutenant?"

They both got up and prepared to leave the tent.

"Rock, 8 a.m. tomorrow?" said Jake.

"Yes," said Kit. "I'll be there." But there was a heavy frown on his face as he watched the two men leave.

That frown deepened as Pico came back to the tent and said: "Boss ride tomorrow?"

"Yes," said Kit very shortly.

"Take Pico?"

"No," said Kit.

Kit had expected Pico to protest, but, to his amazement, Pico merely said: "Boss decides," as he quietly left the tent.

66

Kit's eyes narrowed.

"Now what in hell," he said to himself, "does that mean?"

He reflected for a few minutes, but his face was very grim and strained as he did so.

"Better get to bed," he said to himself. "That treaty is getting on your nerves."

He lay down on his bunk (with the treaty under his pillow) and tried to sleep. But his sleep was at first light and troubled. He thought that he heard some small movement outside the tent and stiffened, gun at the ready. But the movement (if there had been one) ceased. And at last he did fall asleep.

CHAPTER IV

Kit woke up refreshed on the next morning and called for Oompa.

Oompa came in and placed Kit's breakfast before him, but said nothing whatsoever as he did so.

Oompa, Kit noticed, was still looking very sullen.

"Where's Pico?" said Kit

"Coming," said Pico as he also came in.

Kit looked at Pico. There was a curious expression on his face as he did so. Pico seemed to sense it, because he half-turned away.

"Going now," said Kit shortly.

"Back when?" asked Pico.

"Don't know."

Kit left the tent and mounted his horse. His two servants stood and watched him go. Neither smiled nor waved.

Kit rode off towards the Rock. But, as he rode, he was savagely asking himself a question. *Why had Pico looked tired?* In all his life Kit had never before known the Indian's tremendous frame to show signs of fatigue. But Pico *had* looked tired. Why?

Still brooding savagely, he rounded the little knoll that led to the trail that in its turn led to the Rock. But as he reached the trail he suddenly reined in his horse, as he saw the object that was lying across the trail. His own horse was sweating with fear and excitement: she had recognized the object too.

Kit dismounted, led the frightened animal gently round the

67

other dead one, remounted her and rode off. As he rode, he spoke to her soothingly and she slowly calmed down.

"That was a shock, Bessie"—her full name was Old Battling Bessie—"to find *him* there."

The "him" had been Pico's horse, and the bullet wound in his head had shown how he had been killed.

"And what in tarnation, Bessie, all that adds up to," said Kit grimly, "I just don't know. But——"

He didn't complete the sentence. He had reached the Rock, and there was Jake waiting for him.

Jake was in very good spirits.

"Everything okay, Kit?"

Kit was tempted to mention the dead horse, but suddenly decided not to.

"Everything quite okay, Jake. Let's get moving."

They reached White Falls by the early evening. Neither had spoken much during the ride, but at their one short halt to feed and water the horses Jake had said: "You're looking worried, Kit. Anything wrong?" And had got the rather brusque answer: "Nothing wrong, but I *am* worried."

"Why?"

"This treaty, Jake, is a big responsibility. I can't help feeling worried, and I won't stop feeling worried until I get to Kansas City and safely hand it over."

Jake had looked at his old friend's face. "I understand," he had said, patting him affectionately on the arm. "But all will be all right. Just you wait and see."

They had only been at White Falls for about five minutes when Kit noticed an Indian slowly and steadily running towards them. Kit's gun was out in a flash.

"Put that back," said Jake gently. "That's Alaba, the Chief's own personal runner. Come, Alaba."

Alaba came. Kit was still covering him with his gun. Alaba spoke a few words to Jake in some kind of Indian dialect that seemed to Kit not to be a dialect at all but a mixture (and a corrupt mixture that Kit couldn't understand) of various different dialects.

But when Alaba had finished speaking, Jake grinned

"All goes well," he said. "The Chief himself is on his way, and we are just to wait here till he comes."

The daylight was beginning to fail.

"Shouldn't we go on," said Kit sharply, "and try to get through these swamps before dark?"

Jake laughed scornfully.

"Not today, Kit," he said. "Alaba has just told me that a troop of Southern infantry has been seen moving up towards the south side of the swamps. And the Chief advises that we should make the crossing after dark."

"Okay," said Kit, thoughtfully. "Then we'll wait for the Chief." He looked keenly at Jake. "You're the one that seems worried now, Jake."

"Do you know, Kit, you're right. I am worried now," answered Jake. "There's something here that I just don't understand."

"What's that?"

"That troop of Southern infantry moving up to the swamps —and just now, when you are carrying that treaty."

"Go on," said Kit, but in a very hard voice.

"Well," Jake was speaking very slowly and carefully, "is it just a coincidence, or . . ."

"Or?"

"Or has someone who knows that you are carrying the treaty and are now about to reach White Falls warned the enemy: and is this troop of infantry a trap for you or not?"

"It *could* be," said Kit slowly, "a pure coincidence. You yourself have told me that the Confederates are swarming all over the place."

"Or," replied Jake, "it *could* also be——"

"I think I know," said Kit abruptly, "what you're going to say. Or someone has betrayed my mission. But who," he snapped angrily, "would? Only three people know that I'm here. You, me and the Lieutenant, and neither of you two would betray me."

"But, if you don't mind my saying so," said Jake, "there is at least one other person who knows (or guesses) that you have that treaty and have ridden off with it today."

"Go on," said Kit steadily, "who's that other person?"

"Pico," said Jake, "and maybe Oompa, too."

"Don't talk rubbish," shouted Kit so angrily that Jake was startled. "*My* servants will *never* betray me. Poor old Oompa

69

can't ride anyway." (Kit didn't know that at that exact moment Oompa was in fact seated, and very uncomfortably, on the back of a horse that was slowly approaching a small creek not many miles away from where Kit and Jake were in fact talking.) "And what's more," he shouted, "there *is* somebody else that you haven't mentioned yet who also knows that I'm here."

"Who?" gasped Jake.

"That Chief of yours who's just arriving."

Jake looked anxiously at Kit's rather strained face.

"Kit," he said, "don't for God's sake, let this get you down. That Chief is all right and is only here to help you."

He got up and waited for the Chief's arrival.

The Chief was the handsomest Indian that Kit had ever seen. As he leapt from his magnificent brown horse with a lithe grace that Kit could not help admiring and came towards Kit with outstretched hand, Kit's suspicious attitude relaxed.

"Captain Carson?" said the Chief.

"Yes," answered Kit.

"I am proud, sir," said the Indian, "to be able to help you. Jake will have told you that a troop of Southern infantry is waiting for us when we try to pass the swamps. They're waiting at the Big Creek. But we pass at the Small Creek, two miles east of the big one."

He paused. "If we get through, must go now." He turned towards Kit. "May I ask you question?"

"You may," said Kit guardedly. "What's your question?"

"How come Southern soldiers know you were crossing swamps?"

Kit did not answer. The Chief looked at him very sharply. "Very well, let's go. Not much time left. Follow me."

Kit and Jake followed him.

CHAPTER V

It was already quite dark when the three of them reached the little creek.

"Halt!" said the Chief.

Kit could hear, only a few yards off, the lapping of the water.

"Quiet," said the Chief. "Listen."

70

Kit listened.

Far away (as it seemed) to the west, there was a sudden crackle of gun-fire. After a second or two it died down.

"What was that?" said Jake.

"My men," whispered the Chief, "distracting infantry from creek. Safe to pass now. Come."

As he said so, he turned his horse's head towards the noise of the lapping water; and in a minute all three were beginning the passage of the creek.

To Kit, this passage was an absolute nightmare. At one minute the horses were slithering and floundering over shelves of sunken rock, the next minute pulling themselves out of mud reaching up to their withers, and the next swimming breast-high in a current of water that seemed to obey no known rules and seemed to come from all directions at once. But Kit could not help but admire the steady calm of the Chief and the firm whispered directions that from time to time he gave to the two men behind him.

It was with a great feeling of thankfulness that Kit at last heard him say: "Here we are. Stop."

They were standing in a little pool of water that reached only to the horses' fetlocks.

"Quiet," said the Chief as another crackle of gun-fire broke the silence of the night. "They are still firing."

"Nearer us than before," thought Kit.

"Well, what now, Chief?" he asked.

There was another sudden burst of gun-fire, but this time only a few hundred yards away.

"Something gone wrong," whispered the Chief. "We must ride for it. Jake, you follow me. Captain, we two go first and will ride to the right and draw their fire. *You* ride to the left where is a small track, and we join you again soon as we can. Ready, Captain?"

"Yes," said Kit, but in a voice that was almost a snarl.

The Chief spurred his horse, and, with a great yell, plunged through the shallow water. Yelling too, Jake followed him. Kit saw the two horses disappear to the right and rode quickly off to the left. But, as his horse's hooves touched the firm ground of the track, a rain of bullets assailed him. Kit saw in front of him and strung out along the track some fifty soldiers of the

71

Southern Army. There was nothing to do but to ride straight through them. And Kit at once, firing as fast as he could, proceeded to do so. Two or three of the leaders fell. But Kit, with a quick clutch of the heart, realized that unless something happened he would never get past the remainder.

Something, however, did happen.

From some vantage point somewhere above the track a clear voice called "Men, charge!" And to Kit's amazement the ranks of the Southern infantry were suddenly being overrun by mounted men who seemed to have sprung from nowhere.

"Ride like hell, Captain," shouted the clear voice, "and leave this to me."

Kit rode like hell.

In a few seconds he was quite clear of the enemy soldiers; and in a few minutes halted Bessie and mopped his steaming brow. It had been a close shave and a providential escape. But Kit was still puzzled by what had happened.

The voice that had shouted was familiar to him. He had heard it before. But how had the trap (it was clear to him that it had been a trap) been organized? He was reaching a grim conclusion on the point when out of the darkness Jake's voice called: "Are you all right, Kit?"

Kit smiled to himself as he replied: "Perfectly all right."

In a minute Jake and the Chief were beside him.

"Well, Jake, they didn't get me that time," laughed Kit sardonically.

"Thank the gods for that," said the Chief. "Our plan, Captain, worked. If my men hadn't been there——"

"That was a lucky break for me, Chief," said Kit, "and I can only offer you my thanks."

Jake noticed the odd tone in Kit's voice.

"Going all polite now, Kit, are you?"

"Why not, when your life has been saved?"

The Chief laughed. "Come, Captain. In my camp you will have a good meal."

He gently spurred his horse.

During their brief halt Kit had been admiring that horse. It was a beautiful bay gelding. Kit had never seen such sumptuous trappings on a horse before. Bridle solid silver, saddle of the finest leather Kit had ever seen. Stirrups of what looked to be

72

There was nothing to do but to ride straight through them

beaten gold. Kit glanced at old Bessie with her shabby bridle, her well-worn saddle and the very ordinary lead stirrups that he had bought for her many years ago, and felt a momentary pang of envy. But Bessie just trotted gently after the Chief's horse till a sudden long mournful call rang through the valley. She halted, just as the Chief's horse stumbled.

The Chief dismounted.

"What's wrong?" said Kit.

"Broken bridle," was the crisp answer.

Kit watched him as he bent down to repair the bridle. His eyes narrowed as he watched.

In a second the Chief straightened up again, but just as he swung back into his saddle, the long call rang out again.

"That noise no good," said the Chief as his foot nearly slipped out of the stirrup.

"Ready, Chief?" said Kit.

"All ready now. Come."

It did not take them long to reach the Chief's camp, and soon Kit was eating the finest dinner that he had ever eaten in his life—a dinner that not even Oompa could have surpassed. But as he ate he was thinking of many things that had nothing to do with dinners.

"You liked that?" asked the Chief as Kit finished eating.

"Never," said Kit (and with all sincerity), "have I liked anything better in my life."

"Good," said the Chief. "And now, Captain, bed for you. Still very long ride ahead."

"You're right," said Kit. "I feel sleepy."

The Chief clapped his hands imperiously. A servant came in.

"Kada, take Captain Carson to his wigwam."

Kada escorted Kit to the wigwam.

Kit *did* feel sleepy, and the comfort of the warm wigwam was very soothing to him.

He lay down on the beautifully prepared bed.

The Chief came in.

"Everything all right, Captain?"

"Perfectly, thanks," said Kit, "except"—he suddenly remembered—"old Bessie. Is she all right?"

"Bessie?" said the Chief in a rather startled voice.

"My horse," explained Kit.

The Chief laughed. "That horse of yours having good dinner too. Satisfy you?"

"It does," answered Kit.

The Chief smiled.

"Right. Then bed for you. Good night."

"Good night," said Kit as the Chief left the wigwam.

Kit lay down again on his bed and reflected. There were many things on his mind. But he soon fell asleep. The treaty, at any rate, was safe.

As Kit slept a young lieutenant of the Union Army was smiling to himself as he slowly led back to his Fort a detachment of the 43rd Cavalry Regiment.

"That was a bit of luck," he said to himself, "that I got these sudden orders to go to White Falls and pick up these chaps. If we hadn't been there——"

CHAPTER VI

It was Bessie who first heard the steps outside Kit's wigwam, and she whinnied so loudly that all the other horses in the corral—and particularly the Chief's horse, Copa—were extremely disgusted with her.

But (what is more important) Kit had heard her voice and had suddenly woken up.

His gun was at the ready as the flap of the wigwam softly opened. Someone stood in the doorway.

"Don't move," said Kit sharply, "I've got you covered."

Jake chuckled.

"Good old Kit," he said, "taking no chances."

"It's you, Jake," said Kit.

"Me and no one else," said Jake.

Kit put down his gun and lit the small paraffin lamp that stood by his bedside. As the light flared up, Jake blinked.

"Put it out, Kit," he said sharply.

"Why?"

"Better to talk in the darkness. If that light's seen, neither your life nor mine will be worth twopence."

Kit put the light out.

"What brings you here, Jake?"

"Treachery," answered the voice opposite, "black, rotten,

75

vicious treachery. That business at the swamp was no coincidence, Kit."

"Of course it wasn't," said Kit. "Someone has betrayed me."

"And do you know who it was?" The other's voice was harsh and anxious.

"I don't," said Kit very slowly, "but I have my suspicions."

"And would your suspicions be the same as mine?"

"Shush," said Kit sharply. "Listen!" His gun was again in his hand.

Outside the tent there had been a queer scuffling light noise. Jake swore softly and half-rose.

"Sit," whispered Kit, "I've got the flap covered and am ready for anyone that comes through it."

They sat for a few minutes in dead silence, but no one came. Both men began to relax again.

"A false alarm," said Kit.

"Not on your life," was Jake's quick retort. "That's another part of the treachery."

"Speak your mind, Jake," said Kit, "and speak it fast."

"These men who charged at the creek were not the Chief's men, in spite of what he's been trying to tell us."

"I know."

"Good for you, Kit. How did you know?"

"Never mind. Go on. There may not be much time left for talk."

"The whole thing was a sheer trap from start to finish. The Chief had warned the Confederates to wait there—for *you*. You would have been killed but for these cavalry men, and the Confederates would have got the treaty, and that's all. One of the persons who betrayed you was the Chief; and, Kit, I'm damned sorry that I ever introduced you to him. I *did* believe him to be trustworthy, but I was wrong and I'm sorry. I can't say more, can I?"

"Yes," said Kit. His voice had a very sharp edge to it. "You *can*."

Jake stirred.

"Don't move, Jake," said Kit. "I've got you covered, and I want to ask you just three questions."

"Go on," said Jake calmly. "What's the first one?"

"*You* knew that I was carrying this treaty. Did you tell the Chief?"

"I did not," said Jake. "All that I told him was that I wanted him to help you through these swamps."

"But then," said Kit, "why had he warned the Confederates to be waiting for me?"

"Because," was the quick answer, "somebody else had told him you were carrying a treaty of value to the Confederates."

"And who," said Kit, "was that somebody else?"

Jake paused before answering.

"You heard that Indian call at the valley, didn't you?"

"I did."

"And that was Pico's call, wasn't it?"

Kit said slowly: "So you recognized it too?"

"Of course I recognized it," answered the other contemptuously. "And if *you* can't put two and two together, I can. Pico and the Chief are in league together. Why was Pico, while you were away in the south, hanging round the Chief's camp?"

"Jake, I just don't know," confessed Kit. "I wish I did know."

"And Pico," continued Jake relentlessly, "either knew or guessed that you had that treaty."

Tonelessly Kit answered: "Jake, I think he *did* know."

"Well, there you are," said Jake. He was about to say something else when the queer scuffling noise outside the wigwam started again.

"Quiet," hissed Jake as he softly walked to the wigwam's flap and peered out into the darkness.

After a few moments he turned round and said: "Nothing there."

Kit had meantime been thinking furiously. He felt pretty certain that as Jake had said, the Chief had betrayed him. Pico's call *could* mean that Pico too had betrayed him. But, as for Jake himself, Kit was far from decided. Jake was a very old friend; and it was almost incredible that he would do anything to harm Kit. But Kit's mind was by now so suspicious that he was not prepared to trust anyone.

"Jake," he said, "I am getting out of here—and now. But you stay exactly where you are. I'm taking no chances with anyone now."

"Not even an old friend?"

"Not even an old friend. And if you make the slightest move, I shoot."

"I won't move."

Kit began to walk quietly and steadily towards the door, still covering Jake with his gun. He had almost reached the door when he heard Jake draw a sharp breath as he hissed:

"For God's sake, Kit, look behind you."

It was an old trick, but it worked.

Kit glanced over his shoulder for a second, but in that second Jake leapt.

Kit's right hand was grasped by fingers as hard as steel, and Kit's gun fell to the floor.

"And now, Mister Captain Carson," said Jake, "let's have that treaty. It's worth a million dollars to me."

"You swine," breathed Kit.

"Swine or no swine," was the exultant answer, "give me that treaty."

"You'll only get it," rapped Kit, "over my dead body."

Jake said: "Kit, I don't want to kill you, but I do want that million dollars. And, if you don't give me the treaty, I will certainly kill you."

"Go on. Kill."

"That your answer?"

"Yes," said Kit firmly. "That's my answer."

"Okay," said Jake as he cocked his gun. But the gun was never fired.

The flap of the wigwam suddenly opened. There was the quick crack of a bullet as Jake fell dead to the floor.

Kit looked at the man by the flap.

"Get out of sight, Oompa," he hissed, "someone's coming."

Oompa dived under the bed.

Gun at the ready, Kit waited for the new arrival. He was cursing himself for the mistake he had just made, and was determined that there would be no more mistakes.

A courteous voice outside the wigwam called out: "Captain, you safe? May I come in?"

"Come in, Chief," said Kit.

The Chief came in.

"What's happened? I heard shot."

78

Without waiting for an answer, he looked round the wigwam and saw Jake's body.

"So you've killed that skunk, Captain. I congratulate you."

The remark was so unexpected that Kit blinked, but gave no other sign of emotion as he quietly said: "Why congratulate me?"

"Because," said the Chief, "skunks are skunks." He kicked the dead body. "And that," he added, "was the biggest skunk of all."

Kit noticed that the Chief was unarmed and slightly lowered his gun. The Chief noticed the gesture.

"Thank you, Captain," he said calmly, "but keep me covered if you wish. I bring no harm to you."

Kit watched him steadily. There was an expression of both suspicion and wonderment on his face. The Chief noticed the expression; and, with a smile on his face, said: "Shall I continue?"

"Yes," was the short answer.

"That skunk was a trader. He bought and"—the words were spoken with indefinable scorn—"he sold; and he sell his oldest friend for a million dollars."

"I know that now," said Kit. "Go on."

"It was he, Captain, who told Confederates of that treaty."

"Why do you think that I have a treaty?" rapped Kit suddenly.

The Chief smiled.

"What else *can* it be? The Pueblo Indians must be kept out of war. Who could do that but *you*? And here *you* are—on way to Kansas City—and your pouch, Captain, contains buffalo skin, doesn't it?"

Kit hesitated.

The Chief laughed.

"I have keen eyes, Captain."

"You *have* keen eyes," said Kit guardedly, "and, I think, a keen intelligence too."

The Chief bowed in deference to the compliment.

"Sufficient intelligence, I hope, to know also what Jake told you."

"Tell me," said Kit.

"That it was I," answered the Chief sombrely, "who had betrayed you."

"You're right," said Kit brutally, "he did."

"But I," said the Chief, "am no trader. I neither buy nor sell."

Kit looked wonderingly at him. Had all his suspicions been wrong?

There was a moment's silence in the wigwam.

"Look, Captain," continued the Chief steadily, "the Confederates know everything about you. Wouldn't it be better to let me have that treaty?"

"Why?"

"If you take it to Kansas, you will certainly be killed. If I do, no one suspect me."

"But if you do," said Kit savagely, "will your horse's bridle break again?"

His gun was pointing straight at the Chief.

The Chief smiled.

"So you noticed that?"

"I did. The bridle was not broken at all."

"Give me that treaty," said the Chief suddenly, "or——"

"Or what?"

"Alaba!" shouted the Chief. A bullet whistled through the tent. It went wide of Kit, but struck Oompa. But Kit had also fired. His bullet had caught the Chief in the wrist and sent him reeling to the ground. There was the crack of another bullet somewhere outside the wigwam.

Kit's face was very white and tense as he looked at the Chief.

"So you were a traitor too. What did you want that treaty for?"

The Chief sneered but said nothing.

"You were prepared to kill to get it," continued Kit.

He raised his gun.

"I can kill, too."

"*You* won't," said Pico, as his great figure quietly entered the wigwam. He was holding a gun that was still smoking. He covered Kit with it.

Kit swore savagely to himself. Was this another trap? His finger tightened round the trigger of his own gun.

"Wait, Boss," said Oompa as he crawled from under the bed.

Kit waited.

Pico turned towards the Chief.

"We meet again, Big Red Eagle," he said quietly. "Look round. Your camp's on fire."

It was true. Flames were roaring towards the wigwam. Frightened feet were scurrying here and there, frightened voices were shouting and frightened men were aimlessly and wildly firing their guns as they rode desperately through the flames.

"No camp left," said Pico, "and soon no Big Chief left either."

The Chief's handsome face had crumbled into nothing but a pair of pleading and terrified eyes, and Kit heard a croaking and almost inaudible voice whisper: "Spare me. Spare me."

"Why?" answered Pico. "Did *you* spare my camp, my squaw and my papoose fifteen years ago?"

There was no answer.

Pico looked at the Chief with an expression of the deepest contempt as he fired, straight through the Chief's heart. The Chief fell to the ground.

Pico stooped and gazed down for a few seconds at the dead body. When he straightened up, his face was quite expressionless.

"Better go now," he said. "Fire coming very fast."

The fire was indeed coming very fast. The long leaping flames were only a few yards away from the wigwam.

"Where's Bessie?" shouted Kit. A very loud neigh outside the wigwam gave him the answer.

"Bessie outside," said Pico, "also Copa. Come, Oompa."

Oompa was swaying on his feet, and both Kit and Pico saw for the first time the blood that was coming from his shoulder.

"Who did that?" said Pico sharply.

"Must have been that bullet of Alaba's," answered Kit. "Where *is* Alaba by the way?"

"Dead—outside," grunted Pico. "And where's Jake?"

"Dead—here," replied Kit.

"And who killed him?"

"Me," said Oompa. "Jake bad: so I kill."

"Come, Oompa," repeated Pico.

"Can't walk," was Oompa's whispered reply.

"Then I carry you," said Pico. He picked up the little Eskimo in his arms. "Hurry, Boss, the flames are here."

They were. The wigwam was already smouldering, and in a few seconds its flimsy and inflammable structure would be completely ablaze.

"Hurry," yelled Pico.

Kit hurried.

Bessie was glad to see him. She hated these flames and the odd bullets that were being fired by the panic-stricken tribesmen. Kit mounted her. "Coming, Pico?"

"Coming," said Pico as he gently placed Oompa in front of him on the Chief's horse. "Ride, Boss," he shouted, "and ride fast. We're following you."

Kit rode fast, and Bessie galloped as she had never galloped in the whole of her life before.

Behind him, Kit could hear the solid steady pounding of Copa's hooves. The pounding faltered only once—and only for a few seconds as a stray bullet sang past Bessie's ears (and very much to Bessie's annoyance).

CHAPTER VII

They had reached a small stream, some miles away from the Chief's camp.

"Let's stop here for a minute, Boss," said Pico. "The horses need water."

Kit stopped and dismounted.

He himself was glad of a little rest after the events of the night.

"How's Oompa?" he said as Pico dismounted too and placed the little man on the grassy verge beside the stream.

"Bad wound," grunted Pico. "We must let him rest here for a little."

"Can you do anything for him?" asked Kit.

"There's nothing much," answered Pico, "that I can do except to bind it up, then let him rest for a little until we can get him to a doctor."

Kit watched Pico's strong fingers binding up the wound. When Pico had finished, he said: "While he's resting, Pico, tell me one or two things."

"What things?"

"Everything," replied Kit rather irritably. "Why you didn't

82

come with me to Great Antelope, for instance. Why you went to the Chief's camp instead. Why——"

Pico held up a hand to his face as he coughed.

"I tell everything, but must tell fast. For Oompa's sake," he explained as he coughed again. "The night you left to speak to Great Antelope, Oompa tell me strange Indian near Jake's camp. I go look for strange Indian. I see him. Alaba—that rat. I recognize him as one of the men who——"

"I understand," broke in Kit gently.

"Two days I follow him. He leads me to Chief's camp. I see Chief. I recognize him too, but too far off to fire. I follow Alaba back. Back to Jake's camp. Then I come and wait for you."

He paused and coughed again.

"Then Jake come. I hear all. I know Jake traitor. I follow Jake on my horse. I want to hear what Alaba say to Jake."

"And Jake," said Kit, "killed your horse."

"I was a little careless. Jake heard me behind him—fired—killed horse—I pretended to be dead too till he went on."

"Then?"

"I follow him."

"But you had no horse," said Kit sharply.

"I have feet," said Pico proudly, "feet that can walk and feet that can run. Nearly as fast as a horse's feet can run. I hear what Jake say to Alaba. I run back."

Kit remembered Pico's tired look.

"Then *you* go, and *you* say: 'Pico, don't come.' I don't come. I speak to Oompa. We decide we go together to the small creek. We steal horses—many horses—but we get to the creek."

"But Oompa can't ride," said Kit.

Pico coughed again. (Why, wondered Kit, does Pico keep on coughing?) But Pico's level voice continued.

"Two can ride on one horse. I know creek. We reach it. We wait for the ambush. Ready to help Boss. But soldiers help instead. I make long call to frighten Red Eagle. We follow Boss to camp. Oompa wait outside Boss's tent. Kills Jake."

Oompa suddenly stirred. "Oompa bad," said Pico.

"Finish," said Kit.

"I set fire to Red Eagle's camp. Then kill him. **Red Eagle** simple traitor. He want that money too. Hurry, Boss, Oompa very bad."

Kit swung swiftly into Bessie's saddle as Pico, with great care and tenderness, hoisted Oompa on to the Chief's horse, and then mounted himself.

"Go on ahead, Boss," Pico said, "we follow."

It was only a thirty-mile ride to Kansas City, but the night was becoming very stormy. Lashed by torrents of sleet, buffeted by heavy winds and with the darkness often punctuated by long shafts of lightning, it took them five hours to reach the city's outskirts. But, at last, they did.

Guards were everywhere, but as soon as Kit mentioned his name a free passage was given to the riders; and in a few minutes the two steaming horses halted outside General Grant's own tent.

"General," called an officer, "Captain Carson's here."

"Bring him in," said the General.

"There are two other men with him."

"My servants," said Kit.

"Then bring them in, too."

Kit dismounted. So did Pico, and the three of them, with Pico carrying Oompa in his arms, entered the tent.

General Grant glanced rapidly at them. His eyes were the sharpest eyes that Kit had ever seen.

"That man's wounded. Put him down there." He motioned to a small camp-bed. Pico obediently put Oompa on the bed and stood over him: but a small moaning noise suddenly came from Oompa's throat. His head fell back.

"Sorry, Carson," said the General, "but your servant's dead."

"Dead," said Pico in a wondering voice as, to the horror and amazement of both men, his great frame suddenly crumpled up and slid slowly to the floor.

"And I'm afraid," said the General, "that *he's* dead too. Look at that wound in his chest. How did he get it?"

Kit's face was ashen-white.

"Must have been that stray bullet outside the Chief's camp," he half-murmured to himself, "though how he managed to carry Oompa all that way with that wound, I'll never know."

"Carson," said the General curtly, "there's no use brooding. These things happen in war. Your servants served you well, but the war goes on, and there's still much to do. You're leaving tomorrow for Delaware with the 2nd Cavalry Regiment. Okay?"

"Okay," answered Kit.

"Then let's see that treaty."

Kit handed it over. The General glanced rapidly through it.

"Excellent," he breathed.

He looked at Kit. There was an exultant smile on his face. "Carson," he said, "This war will last a long time yet, but it's already won for us, and this treaty has won it."

CLOUD OF DUST

The question is: Was John Marsh a traitor or was he not? It is a problem that may not cost you any beauty sleep, but it makes my curiosity itch. You see, I am a Marsh. And it is not the sort of thing that a man likes to hear when his great-great-grandfather is called a low-down traitor.

Ever since my little Johnny came home from school all-of-a-jitter asking if it was true, I made up my mind that as soon as the chance came my way I would find out the answer. That decision was made some years ago; and most likely it would have lain like a piece of old paper in the drawer of a desk for ever, if something rather extraordinary had not happened.

My job is that of a road engineer. I work with one of the biggest firms of civil engineers in California: most of our work comes from the state and city governments. We have been working on the Alteda River project for a couple of years now. You have heard of the Tennessee Valley Scheme, haven't you? Well, the Alteda project was modelled on that. The idea was to hold back the waters of the river in a great artificial reservoir, which was to be used for generating power and for irrigating the desert land of the California lowlands.

Apart from the dam, power station, irrigation channels the scheme provided for the building of several new townships along the banks of the river and of an eight-stream arterial road linking the towns. It was in connection with this road that I arrived on the Alteda River Valley.

The director of the project made it clear that he wanted the best of everything. When it came to the road, he called me into his office and told me that I was to make it as straight as the Roman roads. The Romans did not have to worry about private land and houses, I told him. Nor do you, he replied. Most of the land beside the river banks had been abandoned. The river had changed its course so often that the farmers had called it a day, and moved their herds up to the hills where there was no danger of flooding. So I was given to understand that the road would not meet many obstructions from private owners, and where it did I was to buy out the obstructors.

I spent a pleasant summer mapping out the course of the road with pegs and lines. As far as I was concerned the job could have gone on for ever. The grass in the sodden fields was lush, and there was no sound to disturb the summer stillness except the humming of the bees.

Twenty miles out from Santa Angela on a stretch of the future road marked on my plans as HX/426 I ran straight into a mansion the size of the White House. I checked my measurements. If only my lines were a few feet out, the road would just fit round the edge of the building. But, as luck would have it, this was the one time when my calculations proved faultless. It was a nuisance. The house would have to come down.

There was a half-Chinese old man living in one room of the place. I asked him if he owned the house. Yes, he told me, he had bought the building and 400 acres around with his life's savings. It seemed a queer thing to do. The land was going to rack and ruin; as for the house, I had to sweep my way through the cobwebs even to have a look at it. I reckoned that he had bought himself a white elephant, and that he ought to jump at the government's offer to buy him out at compensation valuation. But I reckoned wrongly.

"Impossible for me to go," he said in that quick, half-whispered way of speaking that the Chinese have, wringing his hands together, "quite impossible." "Sorry, Dad," I explained, "you have just got to go." "Undertaker have to cally me out first." A smile crossed his face, but before it had reached the other side he had slammed the front door, and I was scratching my head on the doorstep.

"Who does he think he is?" I asked my leading foreman. "The Emperor of China," was Charley Neilsen's reply. "Well, his majesty will have to go into exile," I retorted. The next day the project officer in charge of compensation knocked on the front door of the house. I stood behind one of the pillars of the portico out of the way. "Me not in," the old man called through a chink in the doorway just wide enough to slip in the Sunday edition of the *New York Times*. The compensation officer hammered at the door, then he hollered through the keyhole, then he went and rapped on a window. But the old boy paid not the slightest attention. After about ten minutes wreaths of smoke started curling out of one of the chimneys, and before much

87

longer the air began to smell sweet and sickly. "Guess he is burning joss sticks," I called to the lawyer, "you had best go home and write him a letter; that is the only way you will get him to understand. Tell him that he has to be out inside a week, otherwise the house will come down with him inside it."

A week passed by, and by then the road had caught up with the house. What had been a lazy meadow a week beforehand was littered with bulldozers and concrete-spreaders and cement-mixers and all the apparatus of twentieth-century roadmaking. I strode up to the door again and gave the knocker a good bang. There came no answer. "Guess the old boy has seen sense," I said to Neilsen. "Guess so," he replied. I rattled the door-knob, but evidently the lock was turned. I strode off and went to have a look through a window, but it was impossible to see through —there was a thick blind pulled down on the inside. "I could swear that it was not there last week, Charley," I called. Neilsen was walking round the other side of the house. "The old fellow has pulled all the curtains," Neilsen shouted.

"Amazing thing," I muttered to myself. "Perhaps the old man had been round pulling the curtains before he moved out, but then how comes the door to be locked?" "Bolted!" announced Neilsen, playing around with a piece of wire in the keyhole. "He must have barricaded himself in." I reluctantly announced my conclusion.

One does not break into a man's house with a pick-axe without giving him a little warning, but I doubted if warning would change the situation. It did not. After a quarter of an hour I gave a nod to the boys and they started to smash at the door. With a few expert strokes they had ripped the door off its hinges. It fell on the stone floor of the veranda with a bang that must have shaken the sleepiest frog in the Alteda Valley. When our nerves had settled down, we peered into the darkness. There behind the doorway stood a mountain of furniture as thick as the fortifications of an old castle. We could not see the old boy, but just then he sang out in his croaky, little voice: "I give you many hundred dollars: you leave Old Ling-Ho live in peace." "Too late now," called one of the boys: "you have better hop out quick, Dad, otherwise Uncle Sam won't give you five cents." "Just a moment!" I intervened.

A plan had come to me. If I pretended to accept the old boy's offer, he would have to let me in to give me the money. The plan worked. He told me to go round to one of the side doors, and after some hectic shifting of furniture the door opened wide enough to let me in.

It was as dark as the grave inside. As I walked the cobwebs flicked across my face. "Can't we have some light, Ling-Ho?" I asked. "Follow me," he said, making a dive through the cobwebs like an explorer through the jungle. We came out into a hallway with a great flight of stairs twisting up to a glass roof which let in just enough light for me to focus the lighter on to my cigarette end. "Now, look here, Dad, it's no use——" I started off. But he cut in on me. "This house velly valuable. You not have enough money to buy," he said. "Well, if it is a question of compensation, we can talk it over sensibly." I puffed out some smoke with a sigh of relief. "You give one million dollars?" His voice rose to a high-pitched squeak.

"One million dollars." I repeated the words in a stun. "Now, talk sense," I said, "the whole place lock, stock and barrel with the land thrown in is not worth ten thousand; tell you what— we will offer you fifteen." "One million dollars. No other plice." Ling-Ho's voice had dropped to a hoarse whisper. "He is screwy," I could hardly help myself from speaking aloud. But talking was a waste of time; I decided that I had better grip the old boy underneath the armpits and carry him out. Just then he pressed something into my hands.

"What's this?" I exclaimed. "Five hundred dollars. All collect," Ling-Ho replied. "Now, you go, please!" That just about put the lid on it. I was about to get hold of him by the seat of his pants, when it struck me that there must be something fairly valuable in the place, otherwise the old boy would never offer five hundred bucks to keep me away. "What's special about this house anyway, Ling-Ho?" I asked. "Why is it worth a million dollars?" "John Marsh house. John Marsh belly fortune," he answered rapidly.

My ears pricked up. "Do you mean the famous John Marsh?" I asked. "Yes, mister," he replied. What an extraordinary coincidence! Somewhere in the back of my mind I knew that Marsh had built himself a kind of palace in the lower foot-hills of the Sierra Nevada, but I had never thought to come across it under these circumstances.

"Look here, Ling-Ho." I did not want the old boy to see that I was too interested. "I can't see what that has got to do with it. If there are valuables in the house, you can take them away." Ling-Ho stood there with his head downcast for a few moments. At last he said: "Gold not in house."

"Then what are you worrying about?" I pressed. "Cannot tell you," he whispered fiercely like a snake disturbed. "You take money and go now, please!" I stood my ground. If I was going, he was coming along with me. But this was intriguing. Did this wizened old Chinaman really know something new about John Marsh, something that would either prove him to be a patriot or damn him for ever as a traitor? It certainly was an intriguing situation.

"Are you okay, Boss?" I could hear Neilsen's voice drift in from around the front. "Sure," I shouted back. It was then that I decided that I would tell Ling-Ho who I was. At first he would not believe me; but when I pulled some letters out of my pocket addressed to Franklin Marsh, jnr., he was convinced.

But in a way the knowledge that I was old John Marsh's great-great-grandson only made things worse. He thought that I had come to claim the hidden fortune on behalf of the family. The Chinaman retreated deeper into his shell like a tortoise. Luckily I guessed what was troubling him. "It's all right, Ling-Ho," I hastened to reassure him. "If you find anything you can keep it." "You sign paper, please," he hissed. "Sure, if you want it that way." I was ready to do anything to clear up the difficulty. He darted away to find a piece of paper.

In a few moments he was back with a dirty old sheet covered with an untidy scrawl. It read: "I, Franklin Marsh, jnr., give all claims on estate of ancestors to Ling-Ho." "Does that make you feel any better?" I inquired, after signing my name with a flourish.

He tucked the document carefully away in his pocket. "Now," he announced, "if you help, I pay you; I make you rich; come, please!" He led the way into a dark room. The room was empty as far as I could make out. It was evident that the furniture had been dragged out to help build the barricade. But there was an upright desk standing against one wall. Ling-Ho pulled up the flap, opened one of the drawers inside; at the end of the drawer was a little compartment. It was too dark to see what Ling-Ho took out of it.

"Come, please!" Ling-Ho's voice had a note of urgency as he shuffled his feet over the parquet floor of what had once been a gracious drawing-room. We were back in the hallway again.

Neilsen was getting frantic. I could hear him shouting as he hammered on one of the window-panes. Ling-Ho turned round towards me. "Tell him to go, please!"

I went back into the room from which we had just come and pulled open the shutters; they yielded unwillingly, squeaking and scraping. The window would not open, so I banged on it till Neilsen came round on the outside. "You had better send the bulldozers and the demolition gang away for a few hours," I shouted through the glass. "Tell them to move up to the next section and get started up there." "What's going on?" Neilsen yelled. "I can't tell you just now." As a matter of fact, I could not have explained even if I had wanted to. "How long you going to be?" Neilsen wanted to know. That was a tricky question. "Can't say for sure," I told him. "Something funny about the foundations of this joint—I've got to go down to the cellar to look-see."

It was a coincidence telling Neilsen about the cellar, because it turned out that Ling-Ho had been fetching the cellar key from the secret drawer of the desk. When we got down there he lit an old-fashioned paraffin lamp. It shed a cold white light on a circle of paved floor; there was no furniture. Ling-Ho bent down and levered up one of the flagstones. From underneath he pulled a large, black, leather-bound book—the size of an old family Bible. Carefully he replaced the stone before leading the way up the steps on the ground floor.

I tried to get him to tell me what was in the book and why all the fuss, but he would not be drawn. He just beckoned me to follow. When we got back to the desk in the empty room upstairs, he fetched two chairs. He motioned me to sit down.

"This John Marsh's diary," he announced as he opened the heavy cover. "You don't say," I remarked sarcastically. "Look, please!" He beckoned me to lean forward. The shaft of light from the window with the open shutters spotlighted the page. I peered at the writing. It had gone brown with age, but it was a firm hand, clearly legible. I read the first words on the page, then I read them again; then I looked farther down. The words would not make sense; they were not in a language that I could understand. "I can't make head nor tail out of it," I announced. "What lingo is it?" "Writing in code," Ling-Ho replied laconically." "Yes, I thought as much," I said in between lighting another cigarette.

"Well, what's it all mean, Ling-Ho?" I asked. "You help translate, please!" The Chinaman had got it all worked out. I told him what I thought of that scheme. I was a road engineer, not a cryptographer. There was no use my sitting down to puzzle out Marsh's code; besides there was no knowing whether it contained anything of interest. "Book very interesting," Ling-Ho said precisely. "Look, please!" He fetched an old letter from out of the desk. It was in Marsh's handwriting, but had never been finished.

January 22nd, 1852

DEAR CAROLINE,

I trust that the abominable climate of New York spares you and your husband. Secretly I have long wished that it might be otherwise, so that you would decide to abandon your eastern domicile and set up home with me, as I have so often asked. But if it is not to be, it is not to be.

I fear, dear Caroline, that life in California is far from safe just at present, but any danger that you would suffer in this sense would, I am confident, be recompensed by the great joy that you would feel on seeing your father once again, and perhaps for the last time. I write these words "for the last time" conscious that they will shock you. The cause for my writing them I cannot fully explain to you in a letter.

However, if it should be that you do not come before I am gone, you will find the answer to your speculation written in my diary. Also in that book you will come on directions where to discover a treasure that will keep you and yours in comfort, indeed in affluence for many generations. This treasure I have hidden away, for there is no one here that I can trust.

The key to the code in which the diary is written you already have. It is that same code that I employed when writing to your mother during the campaigns in the North Western territories.

And there the letter stopped. I handed it back to Ling-Ho. "Let me have another look at that book," I commanded. I turned over the leaves. The only comprehensible writing was an ordinary date written here and there at the top of the page. If the directions about the treasure were there, it would mean decoding the whole book to find them. Ling-Ho watched me as I went from page to page. "Young Mr. Marsh interested now, yes?" There was a ring of irony in his voice.

"Yes, I'm sure interested," I answered, hardly looking up from the book. "But where do we go from here? What's the next trick that you pull out of the bag?" "No more tricks, only hard work," he said. "It certainly would be hard work to decode that book," I told him. "But surely you must have made some progress at the job?" I asked. "Take time, take much time," he explained. I saw his point.

Ling-Ho told me that after trying and failing to decode the diary he had turned to searching the mansion for the hiding-place. He felt sure that it was to be found somewhere in the building. His preliminary search yielded nothing; now he was in process of knocking away parts of the wall. He showed me into a room where he had taken down the whole chimney-breast.

"You try make book into English, please," he brought me back to the diary, "and I pay you five thousand dollars." Of course, the money he was gaily offering was to come out of the treasure, when found; so it was not all that of a tempting offer, even if I had been open to bribes. In my job bribery is about as common as flies in summer; I had gotten accustomed to it and hardened against it.

"No do, Ling-Ho." I imitated his way of speaking. He looked disconsolate. I could not help but feel sorry, so I added that I would not mind having a look at the book to see what could be made out of it, but I was not promising any results. "Very good," he said, reassured, "I leave you alone to work." And with that he was up and off.

Breaking codes was not in my line, but I had a fair background of maths. The first thing to be done, I reckoned, was to take a count of the various letters used on a sample page. It showed up that "f" was the most frequent letter. I tried writing the letter "e" in pencil under the "f's" in the diary, because "e" is the most common letter in English.

"E" is one letter in the alphabet before "f". I tried writing in "a" under each "b", "b" under each "c" and so on, but the result was more gibberish than ever. It was not going to be easy—time was needed—more time than was available before the demolition gang reported back.

Might there not be a clue somewhere in the house? If there was one letter in Marsh's handwriting, surely there must be others which he had received. And if one of those was in the same code, I might be able to do some guessing from the code version of the date or some stock phrase that one might expect to find at the beginning or end of a letter.

"Ling-Ho," I called, "come here!" The old man must have been standing just the other side of the door; he came in so quickly; he had probably been looking through the keyhole the whole time. "Yes, please?" He stood there with a look of inquiry on his wizened face. I told him what I was looking for. There were, he said, a great number of letters which he had come across in various drawers. He promised to fetch them.

He came shuffling up first with one bundle, then with another. I could not begin to keep pace with the supply of letters. Some were receipts for purchases, some were reports from the bailiffs of his estate—he must have owned a great tract of land around the house in which we were sitting. One of these reports interested me. It began:

June 30th, 1851

SIR,

I have the honour to acquaint you with the details of the losses inflicted on your herds by last night's raid. As you will already have heard by John Perks, whom I sent with my earlier message, the raiders were well organized, and the raid gave every evidence of being long planned. That it was not the raid of the usual run of cattle thieves is shown by the gang's act in deliberately slaughtering a great number of steers which they could certainly have driven away, had they been so minded. The action of the raiders shows every vestige of having as its motive vengeance and retribution against yourself . . .

The rest of the report concerned the value of the dead cattle and the measures which the bailiff had taken to mend the broken wire fences of the ranch. From this report it was clear that already six months before Marsh had sat down to write that last, unfinished letter to his daughter he was the target for systematic attacks by well-organized enemies. Who were these men? Were they Americans who suspected Marsh of having betrayed fellow settlers to the Mexicans, or were they Mexicans?

I scanned the next letters with intense interest. At last there was a clue. It was a letter in Spanish attached to a large parchment bond. I drew on the little Spanish that I had picked up on a honeymoon in Mexico. The letter was short.

September 3rd, 1843

To Don Jose Marsh.

Sir,

His Excellency the Governor directs me to forward to you by the hand of the bearer the deed of title to 20,000 yokes of land. His Excellency has especially selected for you a tract of land in the Alteda Valley which he believes will prove most suitable for the culture of grapes, knowing how much you appreciate good wine. The grant of land is made to you in satisfaction of services rendered.

I have the honour to be, respected Sir,
Antonio del Somita,
Adjutant to the Governor of
Upper California.

The bond was a highly colourful affair with coats of arms and seals all over it. In one corner was a small inset map which showed in red the tract of 20,000 yokes granted to Marsh. The scale was small, but by the look of it Marsh had been given something like thirty square miles.

From this evidence it looked as if Marsh had undoubtedly been in Mexican pay. So he was a traitor! I might have guessed it all along, but one never likes admitting that one's ancestor was a Benedict Arnold. Just at that moment Ling-Ho came shuffling in with another pile of papers. Sticking out of the bundle was another large deed. It looked as if the Alteda Valley was not the only payment that Marsh had received for services rendered.

I unrolled the deed. This one was in English. It was headed "University of Harvard, Faculty of Medicine". It recorded that on 14 June 1806 the degree of Doctor of Medicine had been awarded to John Marsh, Esquire, of Boston, Massachusetts.

Unlike the other deed this looked rather an amateurish affair. It was difficult to believe that Harvard would have ever issued such a cheap-jack certificate. But wait a moment! I compared the writing on the certificate with Marsh's own hand. Yes, the two could certainly have been written by one man.

I turned to one of the ledger books that Ling-Ho had placed on the desk while I was busy examining the deeds. The first ledger had no heading, but the inside was full. It contained a long list of names, and against each name was a date and a fee in pesos. It looked as if Marsh had gone in for money-lending; small wonder that he had enemies.

The next ledger was full of medical formulae. So, even if the certificate was a forgery, it seemed as if Marsh knew something about medicine. So he should have done. The history books record that Marsh was a first-year medical student when he was sent down from Harvard for rowdyism. "Rusticated" is the word they use when they expel an undergraduate: it comes from Latin and means being sent to the country. According to the story Marsh had taken his expulsion literally and had gone off just about as deep into the Indian country as a white man had ever penetrated. There he established himself with an Indian tribe, took an Indian girl as a wife and set up as a trader. But I never thought that Marsh had taken medicine seriously. There was another book containing details about his herds. He certainly went in for farming in a big way. On one farm he had two thousand head of cattle, on another three thousand. There was an entry showing that on Michaelmas Day 1845 he had slaughtered over a thousand steers and sold their hides to Adam MacPherson, agent of Messrs. Fraser, Ballantyne, Hide Importers of Glasgow, Scotland. On Michaelmas Day 1847, 1848 up to 1851 the book showed a similar delivery to MacPherson. What had happened in 1846? Surprisingly enough, there were practically no entries of any kind for that year.

Next I turned to a book containing quantities of building materials and prices paid. The dates against the entries were in 1844 and early 1845. Soon after getting the grant of the Alteda Valley, Marsh had evidently started building himself a house, this house presumably. He must have been wealthy even then. One of the items was "12 tons of finest Italian marble brought from Carrara at 100 dollars a ton". Certainly the mansion that

They dressed up Ed in a silk hat and morning coat

he had built must have been about the finest in California at that time except perhaps for the Governor's palace at Monterey.

I looked round quickly: Ling-Ho was standing behind my shoulder watching. "Well, what is it?" I asked rather irritably. "Your ancestor velly clever man." He smiled benignly. "Yes, yes!" I said. "Your ancestor velly handsome man, too," he continued. "Look, please!" He fetched a photograph from out of the mountain of papers; it was bent and creased across the middle and rather dog-eared at the corners. Standing in front of an embroidered curtain was a tall, dark man with long, twisted mustachios; in front of him was a throne-like chair, in which was sitting a woman of about forty. Marsh's left hand lay rather patronizingly on the woman's shoulder.

"That doesn't look like a Red Indian," I said to Ling-Ho pointing to the woman. The Chinaman got as near to a laugh as he was capable—a throaty rumble. "Your ancestor have several wives; velly clever man," he declared. I asked if there were any more photos. Ling-Ho went off again to return a few minutes later with a large framed picture of the porch of the house where we were. Underneath the porch was the mustachioed man, evidently Marsh, greeting a party riding up on horseback. Instinctively I turned the photo over to see if there was anything on the back, and there written in Marsh's hand it read: "Al Fortescue leads twenty-seven Americans into California (this party included seven survivors of the ill-fated expedition under the leadership of George Donner)."

The name Al Fortescue rang a bell. I turned back to the ledger containing details about the herds. Yes, there it was; Al was in charge of the Grey Grass Farm in 1847. So, evidently he had taken employment under Marsh; I wondered how many more of the twenty-seven had, too.

Just then there was a tinkling of glass. I looked up: Neilsen had walked through the broken window. On the floor was lying a brick.

"The boys want to know whether to make the level 0·03 or 0·05," he said without introduction, even before he had reached the desk. "Can't you see. . . ?" I was going to choke him off for coming in that way. Poor old Ling-Ho was dancing around like a frightened chicken. But it would not do to be cross with

4

Neilsen; he was a good foreman; there did not come any better. I started doing some calculations on the back of one of Marsh's letters. "Make it 0·05," I announced at the end. "Okay!" Neilsen tossed his head. He started to walk back to the window. "Say, Boss," he stopped half-way to speak. "The director rang down for you this afternoon: he asked where you were. I told him you were out checking levels. You didn't want me to tell him you had got stuck in this barn, did you?" I caught the twinkle in his eye. "Thanks, Charley!" I called after him as he stooped to clamber through the hole in the glass.

"Bring one of your paraffin lamps," I commanded Ling-Ho in a tone so firm that he jumped. "Mister Marsh going to work late?" the Chinaman asked as he trimmed the wick to shed a good light over the desk. "Yeah, I guess so." I could not be bothered to start a discussion; the paper I was reading was too absorbing.

February 20th, 1846

U.S. Consulate,
    Monterey,
        Alta California.
DEAR DR. MARSH,

I acknowledge with gratitude your message brought by Fortescue. How you succeeded in obtaining such information I have no conception. However, I know that you are on most friendly terms with the Governor, and must suppose that you obtained the intelligence from him. They say that he is a man who is over-fond of liquor, so there must always be an element of risk about attaching too much reliability to his words, although they do say "in vino veritas".

In this case the intelligence about British plans corresponds with dispatches recently received from Washington, though there was no precision in the letter from the Secretary of State. I have always suspected that the English would try to get their hands on California. Ever since Sir Francis Drake went back to Plymouth with tales of this prosperous coast the English have dreamed of establishing a colony here. Such an intention, if translated into action, would be wholly repugnant to the United States Government.

I have the authority of the Secretary of State to request you to present yourself to the Governor at your earliest convenience. How you find out from him the precise sum that the British have

*Underneath the porch was the mustachioed man, evidently
Marsh, greeting a party riding up on horseback*

offered, I must leave to you. But whatever that sum is you are hereby authorized by the U.S. Government to offer one million dollars more.

I am, Sir,
Yours obediently,
Thomas O. Larkin,
U.S. Consul.

This put an entirely new light on Marsh's doings. In February 1846 at any rate he had enjoyed the confidence of the American Government. Yet there was no doubt at all that soon afterwards he had lost it in circumstances, which if the reports were true, rendered him no credit whatsoever.

This was becoming really intriguing, so much so that I stopped thinking about the code, and I did not even bother to eat the chop suey that Ling-Ho had set down beside me. "Ling-Ho," I called out, "I want you to fetch every scrap of paper you can find in the house—I'm going into this even if it means sitting here all night and the next night, too." "Thank you, Mister Marsh," he replied, rubbing his hands together and bowing. If Ling-Ho has not been a waiter all his life, I would have eaten my hat.

A small leather-bound book caught my notice; it was about the size of an autograph album and looked rather like one. On its cover a fine pattern had been tooled with gold leaf. Inside, to my surprise, the printing was in Russian. It had a number of figures on most pages. On the fly-leaf was an emblem, a circle of leaves with a small map inside—a map of what looked like the Californian coast.

My knowledge of languages did not stretch to Russian; I could not even make out some of the letters, because they did not look like ordinary English letters. But I was determined to puzzle out what this book was. It looked most of all like the Articles of Association of a Company. Yes, that is what it must have been; the last pages consisted of a list of the names of the shareholders. Now what on earth could Marsh be doing with that?

It would have been most sensible to go through the documents one by one, listing them in order to get a complete picture. That is what I should have done. But I was in a hurry, so anything that attracted my fancy I looked at regardless of where it

100

stood in the mountain of papers strewn around me on the desk. There was a gold-rimmed card. What was that? It was a menu card, that was clear. Written in Spanish it proclaimed that it was a banquet in honour of the Feast of Ascension, 1846.

Around the edge were written the signatures of the guests. I twisted the card round to read the names. There was John Marsh; at the centre was Hidalgo de los Torres, Governor of Alta California. Most of the other names were Spanish. Here was an exception—Arthur Dowding-Merrylees. What was this one? Serge Alexandrovitch Ilyushkin; and next to it an even bigger mouthful, Mikhail Mikhailovitch Baryanovitch.

Arthur What's-his-name was almost certainly English, just as the two gents with unpronounceable names were Russian. I pulled out my diary. When was Ascension Day? May 14th. That was just about three months after Marsh had received the letter from Larkin. He would certainly have had an opportunity to bring up the question of the sale of California with the Governor at the dinner, even if it had not been discussed previously. Yet an Englishman was there, too. Could he have been the representative of Queen Victoria? And what were the Russians there for? Were they also after buying up California?

I looked at the Russian book again. Perhaps it was the Articles of a Russia-California Company, formed to buy up California. If that was so, it must have been rather a strange dinner—with the representatives of three powers bidding against each other to buy the country where they were guests. I laid aside the menu and started to go through other papers.

Here was a collection of pages of pencil-scribbled notes. The writing was so bad that I could hardly read it, but it was Marsh's hand without doubt. I re-trimmed the light to see better. It was the draft constitution of the Republic of California. According to the introduction it was prepared by a group of Americans meeting at Alteda House, the Marsh place, on 21 May 1846. Among those present were Thomas O. Larkin, U.S. Consul at Monterey, and Captain J. C. Fremont, the explorer.

It looked as if Marsh had succeeded in outbidding the English, and here the Americans were settling down to plan what they were going to do with the country. I ploughed through the almost illegible lines. One paragraph read: "No titles to land shall be confirmed until after conclusion of hostilities." That did not sound like a peaceful purchase. Nor did this: "All English property shall stand forfeit to the Republic."

So, that was it. The English must have succeeded in raising Marsh's bid. But how could they? Marsh was told to offer a million more than their highest bid. There must have been some dirty work.

I wished that I had by me a history of California, or even just an encyclopaedia to check up on the dates and what the historians say happened. Ling-Ho told me that there were no reading books at all in the house, though he took me to see a wall of bookshelves seemingly stuffed full of French novels. But when one came to pull out a book, it appeared that they were nothing more than the spines of book jackets stuck on to a board. Marsh was evidently not a great reader, though he liked to appear a man of fashion.

No matter; probably what happened would emerge from these papers. Yet, it was hardly to be expected that Marsh would keep incriminating papers lying around. He was supposed, if the story was true, to have acted as an agent of the Mexicans, and as such to have betrayed his fellow Americans when they attacked the Mexican garrison at a place called Sonoma.

That might explain how the English bid had succeeded. Marsh could deliberately have failed to carry out Larkin's instructions. And, having failed, he no doubt came back with a cock-and-bull story which he presented to the American settlers. They, fearing English domination, determined to take the law into their own hands and seize the country. These notes recorded that decision. Probably Marsh copied them out in fair hand and sent them off poste-haste to the Governor. The louse! I felt like abandoning the search through the papers —and changing my name.

Just at that moment of desperation Ling-Ho came in with a cup of steaming tea. I took a gulp. "Ling-Ho," I said, "Marsh was a rotter; he betrayed the Americans." "No think so," the old man replied; your ancestor sleep with American flag underneath matless." "That's a queer thing to do," I remarked. "Well, how do you reckon that he got together this fortune you are hunting? He couldn't have done it honestly." Ling-Ho had decided views on that. "Oh, no! Gold discovered in California in 1848. Your ancestor have big claim."

That was right. I remembered the date from my school days: 1848. Gold discovered at Sutters Mill, California. So Marsh was in on the gold rush. He seemed to be in on everything. He was an able man, there was no doubt of that. In the Indian wars he had outsmarted the wily warrior Black Hawk; at the end of the campaign the States of Michigan, Minnesota, Wisconsin and Iowa had been annexed to the United States. But then his name had come under a cloud. It was said that at the same time as fighting the Indians he had been selling them arms. For a year or two he was not heard of, and then he turned up in California. That was all I knew about my great-great-grandfather—that, and the tale that he had betrayed the American settlers under Fremont at Sonoma. On the strength of his dealings in the Indian wars the tale sounded not improbable. On the face of the evidence in this desk it looked almost certain.

"I wonder if there is any paper here about his gold claim," I said to Ling-Ho as I started into the pile once more, forgetting for the time being my feeling that Marsh was a traitor. I was looking for a plan showing the extent of the claim, and came on a brown piece of paper with lines drawn all over it. "This looks like it," I muttered to myself. But no! The lines were too straight; it must be the plan of some fortifications. I turned the sheet over, and there it was written in Marsh's hand, "Sonoma fortifications". Scrawled here and there were one or two notes such as "powder magazines—3,000 rounds approx.". And running through a gap in the walls was a line with an arrow at the end of it. This must have been the route for the American attack.

That plan was agreed at the American settlers' meeting, presumably; and that plan was no doubt copied out by Marsh and delivered into the hands of the Governor. I felt hot with anger. Probably somewhere lower down in the pile was a letter from the Governor enclosing thirty pieces of silver or some other reward suitable for this Judas. I found the Governor's letter, dated 27 May 1846.

Governor's Palace,
Monterey.

DEAR DON JUAN,

I write to you as an old personal friend to beg your assistance. Yesterday I received a note from Larkin, your consul, saying that in view of my bargain to sell California to the English, he was advising the President of the United States to take immediate action to preserve the inviolability of the North American continent. The note was couched in the strongest possible terms ending with the clear threat that the President would declare war against Mexico unless California was handed over at once to the United States.

Now, you know that I sent that Englishman packing when he approached me with an offer to cancel the English loan to Mexico in exchange for the sale of the province. I told him to go to Mexico City instead of bothering me. You know too, dear Don Juan, because I assured you of it myself when we dined together on Ascension Day, that nothing would give me greater pleasure than to see the American flag fly under the Californian sky provided that my small condition was agreed. It was you who told me that the condition that I should stay on as American Governor was impossible.

Go please—I beg of you—to see Larkin and repeat to him all that we said that evening. My offer still remains open. Tell Larkin to send another dispatch to the President cancelling his earlier letter. There is no need for war. I only ask to remain Governor for another five years and after that a yearly pension of 25,000 dollars. Surely this is a small thing for such a rich and generous country as yours.

To horse, I beg you, dear Don Juan. See Larkin and do your best for me.

Whatever this letter meant, it certainly did not sound like the pay-off for a traitor. Quite the reverse; in it the Mexican Governor was going down on his knees asking Marsh for favours, and there was no hint of payment for any services.

I loosened my tie and ran my fingers through my hair. The name and honour of the Marshs was saved just when they seemed blackened beyond redemption.

Then, if Marsh did not betray the settlers who invaded Sonoma, someone else must have done. If I could prove who did it, no one would be able to speak evil of John Marsh again.

There was a note addressed to Marsh signed by Fremon. dated 12 June 1846—a fortnight after the Governor's letter. Fremont wrote that he was counting on Marsh to bring a contingent of fifty men to Sonoma. It sounded as if Marsh's force was to be recruited from among his bailiffs and farmers.

Fremont ordered them to rendezvous with the other settlers five miles north-east of Sonoma at 9.30 p.m. on 13 June—the following evening.

What happened at Sonoma I could not discover—there was no report or record among Marsh's papers. From my schooldays I remembered the bare outline. Fremont had entered Sonoma—presumably early in the morning of the fourteenth. There was practically no resistance; it turned out that most of the Mexican officials had fled. The settlers hoisted the Stars and Stripes on the flagpost outside the Governor's mansion, and beneath the American flag they ran up the White Bear, the flag which they had chosen for the new State of California. Later that day the Americans were surprised to be caught between the cross-fire of artillery. Mexican guns had been brought up and were ranging their balls to fall into the market square, around which the small town was built. Someone had given the Mexicans the tip-off; they had brought up their one regiment of artillery, and by evening the Americans were forced to make a horseback dash from the town. The Mexicans re-entered Sonoma. The Republic of California came to an end on the same day as it had begun.

But there was no information among Marsh's papers to fill in the details of the story. I began sorting out the documents into smaller piles—one of papers about the ranch, another letters from his daughter, a third medical notes, and so on. While engaged on this job I came across a pile of papers neatly tied up with a leather lace, all of which were written in Russian. They seemed to have been written by the same man, and from the dates of the year, which was the only thing I could read, it appeared that they were all dated 1845 and 1846. This was certainly mysterious. It had looked as if the Russians had been vieing with the British to buy up California, and yet here was Marsh in what appeared to be friendly correspondence with them. Somehow I must get these letters translated. I suddenly remembered. One of the road gangers was a fellow named Micklov; the other boys used to call him "Russky" because he spent his spare time reading a Russian newspaper sent to him once a week from Paris. He was a refugee from Russia, who had come to America via France. The boys told me that he was really a prince, but I did not know or care—nearly every Russian refugee in America tells you that he is a prince or at least a count.

I called in Ling-Ho and told him that I was going off to see this Micklov in the gangers' camp. The old man was perturbed. "You come back," he inquired. "Sure, sure," I nodded. "Velly well," he added, standing back to let me pass. "I cook you slap-up bleakfast."

Micklov must have thought me crazy. It was nearly midnight when I ran him down in his bunk. True to report he was busy poring over the columns of his Russian paper. I told him what I wanted. He seemed amazed that anyone should want him to use his Russian; most times his language was the butt of joking. Of course, he had not a clue what it was all about; and he could not have guessed how much of a hurry I was in or he would not have offered to bring me translations in a week's time. A week! I went up in the air. By the time I left him he had promised to sit up all night and fetch me round the translations by seven o'clock in the morning. I went off to snatch a few hours' sleep.

From my point of view it was well worth the ten-dollar bill I had slipped to Micklov: the Russian letters were dynamite. It seemed as if Marsh was one of the principal shareholders in the Russia-California Company. The Russians had offered him the equivalent of a quarter of the share-capital in return for procuring investments by other Americans. And it was clear that Marsh had earned his payment. Letter after letter thanked Marsh for bringing American money into the business. By early in the year 1846 the Company had started operations: to begin with, it was buying up quantities of wheat and barley, fruit and vegetables, hides and meat to ship north to the Russian colony in Alaska. In April 1846 the first Russian ship was due in San Francisco harbour to load up the furs which agents of the Company were to buy up from the Indians. Another ship was due in around midsummer with a load of settlers, a party of two hundred Russian liberals who had fallen foul of the tyrannical Tsar.

Around May 1846 the letters from Ilyushkin, who described himself as Director-General of the Company, became alarmed in tone. He had heard of the English plans to buy up California. The Tsar's Ambassador in London had reported that the British

Government was offering in exchange to cancel a loan of £4,000,000 to the Republic of Mexico. A senior official of the British Foreign Office, a man who had formerly been Minister in Madrid, had been sent out to Monterey as Consul. Ilyushkin wrote suggesting that the Americans should join forces with the Russians to defeat this move. He explained that it would be fatal to the interests of the American shareholders in the Russia-California Company if the English were allowed to buy up the province. The Yankees had everything to gain from making common cause with the Russians.

On 10 May Marsh received a letter from Ilyushkin which must have put him on the spot. He had already been entrusted by Larkin, the American Consul, to negotiate on behalf of the United States Government. Now Ilyushkin was inviting him to act as the plenipotentiary of the Russia-California Company.

San Francisco,
10th May 1846

DEAR DR. JOHN,

I am most perturbed by the reports which I am receiving from Sushkin, whom, as you know, I managed to slip into Dowding-Merrylees household as a valet. Merrylees is a very formidable opponent. His knowledge of Spanish is exceptional; the wife whom he married in Madrid is certainly the most attractive woman on the coast—a fact which has not escaped the attention of de los Torres, the Governor.

I hear from Sushkin that de los Torres has already reached a preliminary agreement with the English; he is only waiting now for authority from Mexico City to proceed with the deal. Merrylees has promised de los Torres personally a cash payment of £50,000 and a grant of land in Canada of nearly 25 square miles and—this is the best joke of all—to make him an Admiral of the British Navy! De los Torres does not know one end of a ship from the other: I doubt whether he has ever been on a boat. Yet he has set his heart on an Admiral's uniform, and these unscrupulous English are going to give it to him.

What these England-islanders can do, we can do better. If the key to success in California is de los Torres' vanity, then let us play on it. On behalf of the Russia-California Company I authorize you to offer de los Torres a directorship with an annual salary of a million roubles a year for life in return for the grant of a monopoly concession, under which only ships bearing the Company's flag will be allowed to trade from Californian harbours. In this way de los Torres can remain as Mexican Governor and get even more money than the British offer. As for us, we would gain such a predominant position in the trade of the country that we could afford to pay out several times as much as this million roubles, if we chose.

I urge on you the need for speed. The courier from Mexico City is due at Monterey on 15th June. We must have the concession from de los Torres before then. When the concession is received, I shall recommend the Board of Directors to make you a grant of 50,000 shares.

I remain, as always,
Serge Alexandrovitch Ilyushkin.

Which offer did Marsh communicate to the Mexican Governor —Larkin's or Ilyushkin's? Possibly both. The next letter from Ilyushkin was dated 20 May—a week after the Ascension Day banquet.

DEAR DR. JOHN,

I am inclined to agree with you that de los Torres was nothing like as drunk as he pretended to be. I have been told that the morning after the banquet he was out riding on the Santa Cruz road looking as fresh as a spring flower. Sushkin tells me that Merrylees also went off down the Santa Cruz road that morning. I leave you to add two and two together.

Monterey is ridden with spies. For every one of mine de los Torres has six. I do not know whom to trust. In future we had better correspond in code. Will you please let me know by return which ciphering system you will employ?

As soon as you have a reply from de los Torres let me have it, please, in code.

Written in haste,
as ever,
S. A. Ilyushkin.

Here was mention of code at last. If only there was a copy of Marsh's reply to Ilyushkin, then it would be simple. But there was not. The one but last letter in the packet was a short acknowledgment from Ilyushkin—short and mysterious.

27th May 1846

Your notes received. Direct attack by American settlers is quite hopeless. Will use code for full explanation. I agree on your key selection—the first verse of the psalm with same number as the day. English Bible.

The last letter had a note attached to it by Micklov which said that he could not translate it; the words were not Russian. "Ah! Code," I said to myself. "Now let's see—the first verse of the psalm with the same number as the day."

I shouted out to Ling-Ho: "Isn't there a Bible somewhere in this shack?" Ling-Ho replied: "Only Bible is mine. I fetch." He produced a tiny little pocket edition, printed in Chinese on one side of the page and English on the other side. For someone who wanted to understand Chinese it would have made a wonderful key-book. Whether it would prove so helpful in breaking down Marsh's code I was doubtful, but it was worth a try. "Thank you," I said to old Ling-Ho.

I had another look at the letter that Micklov could not translate. The date was written 28 Маи 1846. That was surely the 28 May. I turned up the 28th Psalm and wrote down the first verse on a piece of clean paper. "Unto thee will I cry, O Lord my rock; be not silent to me: lest if thou be silent to me, I become like them that go down in the pit." Somehow that verse provided the key to the code.

I tried all sorts of systems. At last I got the idea of writing the alphabet down underneath the words of the psalm like this:

UNTOTHEE
ABCDEFGH

But unless something was done to prevent it, both the letter "c" and the letter "e" would be represented in code by "t". So I tried writing down the words of the verse leaving out any letter that had already appeared once. This was how it looked:

UNTO HE WIL CRY DMKBSFUGWP

Under these letters I wrote the alphabet again. Thus "a" became "u", "b" became "n", "c" became "t", and so on. Now, the next thing was to test out the system.

I had to get hold of Micklov. He was the only man who could check whether my solution was correct. I laid down my pencil and ran out of the house, nearly bowling over Ling-Ho in my rush. Outside, Charley Neilsen came up to me. He was getting excited, which was unlike him.

"Look here, Boss," he said. "I can't check the levels on my ownsome." "Okay, Charley," I replied without stopping, "I'll be along. "When?" he bellowed after me. "Soon; won't be long now," I reassured him as I slammed the door of my roadster.

Micklov turned out to be a great help. He had been in the Russian Intelligence in the First World War, and knew something about codes and ciphers. Our first attempt at translating Ilyushkin's letter broke down, but it was obvious from the odd word here and there that came out into ordinary Russian that we were on the right track. It was Micklov who thought of the solution. He tried writing the alphabet again underneath the psalm, leaving out the letters J and X, which were practically never needed. This produced exactly the correct result. Within fifteen minutes Micklov had deciphered the whole letter, and within another five he had shaped it into English. This was what it said.

28th May 1846

Dear Dr. John,

I trust that you will succeed in deciphering this without too much difficulty. Now, dear friend, please persuade your compatriots to abandon this crazy idea of seizing California by force of arms. The effect of such action on the part of the American settlers would be to throw the country into a bitter civil war. The Mexicans would not and could not tolerate the conquest of their most prosperous province by a group of desperadoes (if you will pardon the use of the term). They would consider it a matter of honour to reconquer, and they would bring up an army of landless peasants from the south who would by sheer weight of numbers annihilate your American friends.

Apart from the prospect of eventual failure there is the consideration to bear in mind that all trade would become impossible if the country was plunged into civil war. The Directors of the Russia-California Company would view such a state of affairs with great concern. On behalf of the company I must use every effort to prevent anything like this from coming about. Though, as you know only too well, I have no love for de los Torres; if it came to the choice of siding with him or allowing the country to be torn apart I would have to choose the former.

For goodness' sake get the Americans to abandon this ridiculous plan to storm Sonoma. If necessary, I authorize you to offer up to 500 free shares a head to buy off the hot-heads who want to lead the attack on Sonoma.

Let me know what happens as soon as you can.

As ever,

S. A. Ilyushkin.

The cipher was broken, but the story of the assault on Sonoma became even more mysterious. At one time I thought that Marsh was nothing more than a traitor in the pay of the Mexicans; then with a complete somersault I had come to the conclusion that he was a genuine American patriot; now I could not make up my mind. It was this series of letters from the Russian that made Marsh's position so odd. On whose side was he? Discounting that he was in Mexican pay—and that did not look very likely in the light of de los Torres' begging letter—he might either have been working for the U.S. Government or for the Russia-California Company. He could not have been working for both; that much was clear from Ilyushkin's last letter.

Micklov asked me if he should go back to the road workings. I told him that I would appreciate it if he would hang around. I meant to have a go at the ciphered diary that contained old Marsh's secrets; it might be that it was written with quite a different system of cipher, in which case Micklov would come in handy. I invited Ling-Ho to be present at the ceremony of unveiling the contents of the big black diary. He was overjoyed until he saw Micklov standing beside the desk.

"You send gentleman away, please," Ling-Ho demanded. "Nothing doing, old pal." I was going to be firm. Ling-Ho stared up into the face of the brawny Russian, and what he saw did not please him. He darted forward to put his hands on the diary, saying: "Then I put book away, thank you." I pushed back my chair and got to my feet. "Now, look here, Ling-Ho, I need Mr. Micklov; he is a deciphering ace—besides if it wasn't for him I'd never have discovered how to break the cipher at all."

Ling-Ho was not in the least reassured. "I take book away," he repeated deliberately.

"Very well," I said, "if you want to do that, I'll go away and I'll come back with the demolition gang." The old Chinaman threw up his hands in terror. "You promise to help," he cried. "I know I did," I told him. "But I reckoned that you were going to be sensible." It was then that I realized what was biting Ling-Ho. "You want Mr. Micklov to sign a renunciation paper?" I asked. Ling-Ho let go of the diary while he considered the question. "Velly well," he answered at last.

Micklov had no idea about the hidden treasure, so it cost him nothing to sign a piece of paper saying that he had no claim on the estate of the late John Marsh. Ling-Ho folded the paper up and pushed it away carefully into one of the seams of his jacket. "How you find out seclet?" he inquired. I explained to him that the key to the cipher had been embedded in a letter written in Russian; it was not surprising that he had never come upon it. Ling-Ho thought otherwise. "Ling-Ho velly stupid," he announced, shaking his head. "Po-Yee, young nephew, speak little Russian; should have asked him to help, but no tlust Po-Yee." "That's your trouble," I told him, "you're too suspicious by half."

With that I opened the diary and turned over the pages until I came to the year 1846. There were only two entries for June of that year. The first was very short indeed. It was dated 13 June. I got hold of the Bible again and turned up the 13th Psalm. Once again I copied out the first verse and wrote underneath the alphabet, leaving out the letter J and X. The result was a complete failure: only gibberish emerged.

Ling-Ho's face looked so sad and old; he was very disappointed. I admit that I felt suddenly tired; probably the long hours of poring over papers were beginning to tell. Only Micklov seemed quite undisturbed. He started asking me questions about Marsh. Was he a very religious man, he wanted to know. I did not know the answer, but there was no evidence to suggest that he was. Micklov explained why he had wanted to know. He thought that if Marsh had been very pious he might have objected to using the 13th Psalm because the number 13 was unlucky. "Well, that's always a chance," I said. "What about trying the next entry in the diary?"

The next passage in the black book was headed 28 June. We had the key already worked out on the first verse of the 28th Psalm from the Russian letter, but this time it produced no result. Micklov then asked me whether there were any books of Marsh's still in the house. I told him that there were none, because I had already asked the same question of Ling-Ho. "Then, we had better concentrate on the Bible," Micklov suggested. "What do you mean?" I asked. But Micklov had already got to work, and I saw what he meant.

He was looking at the index page of the Bible, putting a tick against all those books which had more than thirty-one chapters. "We had better try at the beginning," he announced.

The first verse of the 13th chapter of Genesis proved to be the right key. Ling-Ho jumped into the air like a two-year-old when he saw the words appearing in translation. But, when deciphered, there was nothing in the entry to throw more light on the Sonoma mystery. It read:

13th June. 1846. I commend my soul to the Almighty and my possessions according to the will which I wrote this year on 1st March. Tonight I go to join Fremont for the assault on Sonoma. Mrs. Austin has embroidered a fine white bear on a blue calico background to serve as the first flag of independent California. May it all turn out well!

The entry for 28 June was much fuller. But before I could complete deciphering, Neilsen had come striding through the hole in the window. "Message from the Director," he said as he handed me a note. I unfolded the paper. It was brief and to the point. The Governor of California was showing the senior Senator over the project that very afternoon. I was to give a demonstration of roadmaking—something spectacular. I passed the note to Neilsen. The chief foreman's comment was: "I reckon that the most spectacular thing you could show His Nibs would be a stick of dynamite exploding under this palazzo."

I looked at my watch: 11.30 a.m. The Governor was due at 3 p.m. "Right-o, Charley!" I said. "I'll take you up on that. Get the boys to lay the charges and the fuse lines. At 3.05 p.m. you can press the firing lever. If I'm not out of here by then, that's just too bad for me. Now SCRAM!"

The entry for 28 June had been completely deciphered by Micklov.

Everything here is at sixes and sevens. There is a rumour current that the British Atlantic Fleet has rounded Cape Horn on its way up to the Californian coast. I rode over to San Phelippe, where Larkin has set up a temporary consulate, to see whether he could contact Commander Sloat's squadron. It is essential that our American men-of-war put into the coast harbours and land men and guns enough to protect the ports from the British. But Larkin's door-man would insist that he had ridden off that morning. I asked him where, but his reply was vague. While I was standing there Bruce McGrigor walked straight past me. I hailed him, but he would not reply. This confirms my impression that something odd has happened. Since we had to abandon Sonoma a fortnight ago, I have been unable to establish contact with Larkin. True, the country has been terrorized by Mexican soldiers and no one is safe who cannot reply to their challenge in Spanish, but that is no reason why Larkin should not have replied to my two letters. If the Americans do not stand together at this time, then we will all be lost.

From reading that entry it looked as if already the word had got around that Marsh had betrayed Sonoma to the Mexicans. Had he? Surely not. No man who was guilty would have written in his diary in the way Marsh had done on 28 June.

There was a gap of three days in the diary. On 1 July Marsh wrote:

Just back from Santa Cruz where I managed to contact Sloat. Rode over on morning of 29th; had to take cross-country path to avoid Mexican patrols. At Santa Cruz they said that Sloat's squad-ron had sailed that very morning. I persuaded Dogherty, who keeps a light ketch in the harbour, to run me out to sea. We sighted Sloat's flag the next morning. I signalled and Sloat lowered his sails to give us a chance to come alongside. It took an hour to convince him of the danger. But, since he carried orders to declare war on Mexico should the need arise, he was willing to do what I asked. The squadron changed course and we were all back at Santa Cruz roads by nightfall. Sloat will land guns and men enough to protect Santa Cruz, Yerba Buena and Monterey har-bours. Monterey is heavily garrisoned by the Mexicans. Sloat has sent a messenger to invite de los Torres to admit the naval force. If the Mexican refuses, Sloat will bombard the town from land and sea. I am to raise a settlers' brigade and join with Sloat at Monterey on the 4th.

On the next page of the diary there was no fresh date, so presumably it was still written on 1 July.

An incomprehensible message from Fremont. He writes that I am to appear before a Court Martial at Quentin's Ranch charged with treachery. I have refused to go!!! Fremont and his friends would do better to join with me and ride down to Monterey. I have told him so.

The remainder of the page was blank. The following page was headed 3 July 1846.

Fremont and twenty-five men came here this morning. There was a blazing row. They accuse me of having been in de los Torres' pay. It is an utterly monstrous suggestion. I showed them de los Torres last letter to me to prove it. After that they quietened down enough to agree that, if I could find out who did betray the plan of attack on Sonoma, they would give up the idea of a Court Martial. They are going to give me seven days. I begged them to join with me and go to Sloat's aid at Monterey. But, they refused. Fremont said that he had entrusted himself to a traitor once, and that was enough. I challenged him to duel. We were about to fire, when up came a hundred men who had answered my call for volunteers to go down to Monterey. The duel was abandoned. Six of Fremont's men agreed to come with us. We are to leave in an hour's time.

A gap of ten days followed.

July 13th 1846.
    Hurrah! California is ours. Sloat has stormed Monterey. The Mexicans are in confusion. The Stars and Stripes fly! No sign of the English fleet.

The job of deciphering each entry was maddening. I could hear the boys outside; they were laying the dynamite charges. I glanced at my watch: it was already one o'clock. Ling-Ho was getting excited: the boys were digging up the veranda. "All right, all right," I said to cool him down: "just you go off and round up Mr. Micklov and me a tray of grub. That's got him out of the way." I turned to Micklov. "Have you got another entry deciphered?" He replied by handing me a write-out of the page headed 22 July.

July 22nd
   Messenger came overland from Washington. He carries dispatches reporting that the English fleet is still in the Atlantic. So, the report of an English attack was all a mare's nest. But what does it matter? It was the excuse we needed.

July 24th 1846
   Ilyushkin came here today. He has been all the while with de los Torres who has now set up a temporary headquarters near San Diego. He brought a message from the Governor offering the Russia-California Company a monopoly of all trade in California in return for assistance against the Americans. I told Ilyushkin that the offer was absolutely unacceptable. Il. was angry. He told me that it had taken him two weeks' hard negotiating to get these terms from de los Torres. I replied that there was nothing very marvellous in that; the Mexican position was so desperate that de los Torres would probably be willing to sell his mother just to get some help against the American settlers. Il. grew more angry. In the row he revealed that it was he who had given away the Sonoma attack to de los Torres. He knew about it, of course, from my letters. The skunk! I could have strangled him there and then, but I remembered that, if I did, I would have no proof to offer Fremont that I was innocent. Decided to lock Il. in the cellar.
   July 25th, 1846. Ilyushkin escaped! Unbelievable.

So that was it: the Russians had been playing a double game. They had wanted to keep in with both Americans and Mexicans. To get better trade terms out of the Mexicans they were prepared to sell the Americans down the river. Like most people trying to be too clever they failed—failed miserably. Marsh at any rate was innocent. Or nearly—he was to blame for ever going in with the Russian Company, to blame for writing compromising letters to Ilyushkin, to blame for running with the hares and hunting with the hounds. But he was not a traitor.

A week later Marsh poured out his bitterness into his secret diary.

> Throughout it seemed to me that the Russia-California Company presented the best hope for the American settlers. What we needed above all else was capital—money with which to import the cattle, machines and building materials for our new homes. New York bankers were not prepared to take the risk, but the Russian Government was. They poured money into this Californian venture like water. Though I would always have preferred to work to make California a State of the Union, I recognized that without war against Mexico such an end was impossible of achievement. That is why I threw my influence into persuading American settlers to join the Russia-California Company. But I have been tricked, fooled and deceived. Ilyushkin was nothing but the lackey, the creature of the Tsar, who cared nothing for California but only for the aggrandizement of Imperial Russia. Through my being deceived many fine Americans lost their lives at Sonoma, and I am for ever a "pariah", an outcast, a man without status, name or reputation.

That was the last entry for a year. Whether Marsh had been court-martialled there was no telling. Something had certainly happened that discouraged or prevented him writing for such a long time. Perhaps the next entry gave the clue.

> August 23rd, 1847. Sutter's Fort. Col. Sutter sold me 50,000 acres today. The title deeds will not be changed into my name to save complications!

So Marsh had gone off to the mountains prospecting for gold: that was how it looked. For was it not just one year later that gold was first found in the mill race by Sutter's Fort? And what were these "complications" about having land registered in his name? Was he an exile; had he been forced to abandon his vast ranch; was he on the run?

The chain of speculation was interrupted by one of the demolition gang coming into the room trailing one of the fuse wires across the floor. Ling-Ho was most indignant. He rushed up to him and said: "You no see—Mr. Marsh work." "Sure, sure," replied the ganger, "don't get huffy!" "All right, Martin!"

I exclaimed. "I'll be out in a minute or two." Ling-Ho came rushing over to me. "But what about . . . ?" He looked furtively round the room, hesitating. "You know what, Mr. Marsh?" "Just getting to the interesting part, Ling-Ho," I was able to reassure him. "Just squat on the floor and take it easy." I turned to Micklov. "Got anything more there, Ivan?"

Micklov was flicking over the pages. He was now looking at the year 1848. "This looks like he hit the jackpot!" Micklov announced excitedly. "What's he write?" I asked. Micklov pencilled the English equivalents under the cipher letters and read slowly.

> November 7th, 1848. This afternoon at Panhandle Gulch I panned shingle yielding gold in profuse quantity. Two or three of my men were about at the time. So, I said nothing. But I shall return here privately tomorrow.

> November 8th, 1848. Panhandle Gulch is as rich as I had ever dreamed. The only problem now is to mine the gold.

"Do you hear that?" I called to Ling-Ho. "Yessir!" The old man was up on his feet again, standing at my elbow. "But where your ancestor put the gold?" he asked. "That's what we are going to find out, if there is time." "Please, please," he pleaded, "tell men go away, leave house in peace." Before I had time to answer, Neilsen had yelled through the window: "Charges all laid, Boss! Just fifteen minutes to go!"

"Here, Ivan." I was getting impatient. "Give me the diary." I seized it from his hands, and as soon as I had got it firmly I ripped out a section of pages. "I'll get on with these," I said. "You see what you can find in the rest."

For a minute or two there was intense silence, interrupted only by the turning of pages. Then I cried out: "Here we are!" I started pencilling the English equivalents under the words at a furious pace. The sense came slowly and steadily.

> 17th January 1850.
> Once again the house was raided while I was out. The vendetta against me continues. I fear that one day they will burn down the building. Tomorrow I shall move the gold to a new hiding-place.

118

I have already dug a hole under the verandah paving. The entrance to the hole is underneath the portico—the fifth paving-stone in front of the entrance door is marked with a scratch the shape of the letter Z. This stone lifts.

Ling-Ho was staring over my shoulder as I translated the words. As I came to the end he vanished. I looked up at Micklov. "He has waited ten years for this moment," I said "Come, we had better look," said Micklov as he rose from his chair.

Out on the veranda Ling-Ho was stabbing away at the fifth paving-stone with a chisel, trying to prise it up. A hundred yards away the gangers were drawn up in an untidy line with Neilsen pacing up and down in front. I looked at my watch. It was five minutes to three.

It seemed like ages, but at last the stone yielded. With a creak Ling-Ho managed to lift it enough to get his foot underneath one end. I bent down; so did Micklov. "Heave!" I called. The stone came up.

True to prediction, where the stone had lain was a deep black hole. I had a flashlamp in my pocket. Its beam shone into the recess. It was a vault about four feet deep and as many wide. Seeing that it was no deeper, I jumped in and bent down to have a close inspection.

"Sorry," I shouted out with my head still underneath ground. "Sorry! Ling-Ho. Someone has got here before you. The place is empty." I clambered out. Ling-Ho was lying on his tummy peering down into the blackness. In a moment he was up on his feet staring at me with the pathetic eyes of a spaniel. "Not possible, Mister Marsh," were the only words which came through his lips. His mouth was quivering, and the tears came to make a film over his eyes. For a moment I could not speak, either. Then I put my arm round his shoulder, and patted him gently. "Everything is possible in this world," I said reassuringly. "Even you, you old son of a gun, and the most improbable tale that ever came out of California; the tale's true; there is a hole under the veranda. I guess it was that Mexican who was supposed to have killed John Marsh that found out the secret. Come on," I added, "let's go down the steps and have a turn in the garden."

Just then the Governor's car rolled up, flanked by two motor-cycles with whining sirens. The gangers uneasily doffed their caps. "Stand clear!" roared Neilsen. There was an ominous rumbling followed by a peal of thunder. I turned round. Where the house had stood was only a cloud of dust.

"LUCKY CUSS" ED

The cavalry men were lying lazily on the ground. They had had a long ride since dawn; a good meal of boiled beef and coffee cooked over the fire had made them drowsy. The noonday heat out on the Arizona desert was enough to make a man give up the struggle to keep awake.

If I don't start jabbing the needle into these guys, Chief Scout Sieber thought to himself, the troop will never make Bisbee by sundown. Sieber was not popular; the scouts and troopers under him thought him a slave driver; the Colonel, who spent his day cracking weak jokes, grumbled that Sieber never even smiled. But no one would or could deny that he was a most efficient scout. In fact, since Will Cody had taken to touring the stages of the world as "Buffalo Bill", there was not a better scout in the West.

"Hi! You, Ed! Shake yourself!" Sieber kicked away at the sleeping man's boots until he opened his eyes and began to yawn.

"Take it easy, Sarge!" Ed Schiefflin disliked having his dreams interrupted. He used to say that lying asleep dreaming was the happiest time of his life. But, then, he was a dreamy sort of man.

"Don't you 'take it easy' with me!" Sieber roared in a voice that would have done credit to a sergeant-major of the Grenadier Guards. "Jump up, you lazy lizard, and go over to the ammunition box. Take out a couple of bullet bands and stuff them into your haversack."

Ed Schiefflin wandered over to where the ammo chest had been dumped. All around him the men were muttering and cursing as Chief Scout Sieber shook them to their feet. Ed took out a couple of bands and shuffled back. This midday sun was really too much for any man, he was thinking to himself.

The Chief Scout knew what was doing. If the troop had to keep down to the speed of their pack-horse loaded with ammo, they would never reach Bisbee that night. That was why he ordered Ed to stow away some of the ammo in his haversack: if each man took a couple of bands, there would be no need to have a pack-horse.

Sieber blew his whistle twice: that was the signal for mounting. The other twenty men jumped on to their horses, but Ed was still kneeling on the ground struggling to get the ammo into his sack.

Sieber came striding over. "What do you think you're playing at? Can't you hear no more?"

Ed was not going to let himself get flustered.

"Can't get these bands in, Sarge. Ain't room for them."

"Then pull out some of those lousy rocks you've got in there."

Ed would have done anything rather than that. "Can't be done, Sarge. I need 'em."

"Ho! You do, do you? Well, I'll tell you something, Ed, m'lad." Sieber grabbed the haversack and started rooting out the bits of stone inside. "Uncle Sam don't need 'em. See?"

Ed was not the same man after that. When they reached Bisbee that evening, the lads tried to get Ed to cheer up—and Bisbee was quite a cheering town in those days—but Ed just rolled over on to the other side of his bunk and turned his back.

Sieber's troop of scouts had a job to do. Geronimo, the Chief of the Apache Indians, was making life in Arizona rather hot for the white folk. The Colonel had told Sieber to take a troop of his scouts and keep an eye on what the Apache were planning. So day after day Sieber had to take his men riding in great circles round the rock-strewn desert that fringed the mountain lair, where Geronimo had his fort.

Ed's collection of rocks had been his pride. It was true that he had not yet found what he was looking for, but among those lumps thrown out by Sieber were a couple that would have assayed at two thousand dollars a ton.

Ed had been looking for gold ever since he was a kid of twelve. He had run away and left his parents to try his luck up on the Salmon River diggings in Idaho. Since then he had tried his luck quite a number of times. In eight years or so he must have panned more than eight hundred creeks and rivers. Now and again he had found a few grains of gold dust at the bottom of the pan. But for the last year or so he had not even had that much luck.

The only reason why Ed had joined the scouts was because he had run out of gold dust, and the store would not give him any more credit when he wanted a side of bacon or a sack of flour. He did not believe in soldiering. He did not believe in any kind of work except slamming away at rock with the sharp end of a pick and panning the shingle from river-beds. Everything else was "slicker's work" in Ed's estimation. And a "city slicker" was just about as loathsome to a "desert rat" like Ed as a sand snake.

Of the jobs open to Ed, life with the U.S. Cavalry Scouts was the best: it gave him a chance to knock away at rocks during his odd hours, to cover ground where no ordinary miner would care to go without an armed escort. It was not long before he had built up another collection of rocks to replace the lumps thrown out by Chief Scout Sieber.

The other men in the troop used to pull Ed's leg: as they rode along together one of them would call out: "Promising bit of rock over there, Ed! I caught a glint in the sun just now. Streak of pure gold by the look of it."

However often they played the joke Ed would always take it seriously. He would put his hand up to his forehead to keep the sun out of his eyes to see if he could catch the glint.

"Hey, Sarge!" one of the men would shout. "What about a halt? Ed wants to go and find a gold mine." And if Sieber felt that it was time for a break, he would blow his whistle. Ed would jump down from his horse and run over to the spot that had been pointed out. The boys liked him. Even when he had spent his whole dinner-time digging away at a piece of rock as hard and as unpromising as granite, he was not in the slightest annoyed with them.

"You never know when your luck's coming up trumps," he would say, stuffing a great slice of beef into his mouth to make up for the meal that he had missed.

One midday Ed had gone strolling off in search of his luck. It was in a rocky part where the great red cliffs stuck up out of the desert like red teeth from a white gum. No one noticed what had happened to Ed. Sieber blew two blasts on the whistle as usual. The troop got ready to move off, but there was no sign of the prospector. His horse stood there lazily flicking his tail, as if to say, "Don't I just know what you are up to, Ed Schiefflin?"

Sieber looked as if he was going to burst. "What's up with that ass again?" he roared. "I'll have him behind bars when we get in tonight. He is more trouble than a whole tribe of Apache." He pushed the whistle in between his teeth again. "Wwwwhew! Wwwwhew! . . . Wwwwhew! Wwwwhew!"

Ed came running up at a pace that showed that he was not straining any of his muscles.

"Jeepers creepers!" yelled Sieber. "Do you think you'd oblige us by paying just a little attention to this whistle?" And Sieber blew so shrilly that Ed put his hands over his ears.

"Save your breath, Sarge!" Ed announced when he finally reached Sieber. "You'll have no more trouble from me. I'm quittin' here and now."

"If that's your idea of a joke, Schiefflin, I'll make you laugh on the other side of your face." But it was no joke, as Ed explained. By the U.S. service regulations he was entitled to discharge himself whenever and wherever he chose, provided that he was in credit with the Paymaster. Ed was ten dollars to the good, and he chose to be demobilized right there where he stood—out in the Arizona desert, twenty-five miles from the next white man.

Sieber took to the idea. It would learn Schiefflin jolly well right. After a couple of nights he would end up with an Indian arrow through his chest, or else he would come trailing back to Bisbee, begging to be signed on again as a scout. Sieber smiled to himself as he thought of just what he would say to Ed, if he ever applied to be readmitted.

"Righto!" he said out loud. "You can have your ten-dollar bill, and here's luck to you. You'll find no saloon in these parts to blow your dollars. You might as well use the bill to kindle a fire; that's all the good it'll do you out here." He leaned down from his horse to pass Ed the bill. "So long, Ed. I guess you always were crazy." He blew on the whistle again, and the troop started to move off.

"So long!"

"Cheerio!"

The scouts and Ed exchanged good-byes as they rode off.

"Don't forget your pals, Ed!"

Ed was not in the least dismayed to find himself alone in the boundless desert. He preferred to be alone. One never knew who was hanging around to jump one's claim in these days; much better to have no one in sight, Ed decided.

Next morning he set off from the spot where they had left him. There was some rich ore just there; that was why he had decided to throw up the scouts. It was not that he was fed up with Sieber or his whistle; it was just that he had found what he was looking for—a high-grade ore. Somewhere in these parts was the mother lode, the seam itself, and Ed was going to have a mighty good look for it.

Ed was trailing his horse. Every few yards he would drop the reins and get hold of his pick between his two hands. Chip, chip, chip. . . . Bang, bang, bang! But it was no good. He seemed to have lost the trail: the seam of ore was nowhere to be found.

Ed was settling down to his evening meal of crumbled biscuit —the last food left in his sack—when who should come riding up but Sieber. The Chief Scout was on one of his rounds. He was not exactly looking for Ed, but he was glad that he had come upon him: somehow he could not help feeling a little bit worried lest that cussed young gold-miner had got himself killed by the Apache. He jumped down from his horse in what for him was a cheerful mood; other people would call it the sort of mood that a man is in before he has shaved or had breakfast of a morning—but for Sieber it was cheerfulness.

"What are you doing, Ed?" he inquired.

"Prospecting."

125

"Where?"

"Over yonder." Ed pointed towards the forbidding range of rock in the distance.

"What! Them hills?" exclaimed Sieber. "Geronimo is loose in them hills. You won't find nothing there but your tombstone."

"Take my chances," replied Ed, who was determined not to let Sieber know that he was down in the dumps. Sieber tried to persuade him to ride back to Bisbee, but Ed would not budge an inch. Sieber glanced up at the sun: it was beginning to go down behind the hills. It was time that he was getting on.

"Well, I'll wish you luck anyhow, Ed!" And he rode off to Bisbee to tell the boys that Ed Schiefflin was desert crazy and planning to commit suicide by going into the San Pedro hills.

Next morning Ed made a long march forward right into the hills. As he rode he could see the Apache smoke signals announce his coming. Dot . . . dash . . . dot . . . dash . . . The smoke climbed into the sky in long and short columns as the signaller waved his blanket over the fire. Ed looked round, but there was not a soul in sight. And yet there must be. . . . Yes, behind those rocks up there narrow eyes were following him. He shuddered; he could not help himself.

The Apache waited. What was this white skin doing? He kept on stopping, knocking off a chip of rock, holding it up to his eye and then throwing it away. He did not seem interested in anything but rock. After a while a rabbit jumped out of nowhere just in front of Ed and raced away up a little path. Ed came to a halt. A rabbit? Guess I couldn't have been thinking, he muttered to himself. A rabbit. Guess I might as well follow it.

The Apache watched. The paleface was certainly no ordinary hunter; he did not even bring out his gun to fire at the rabbit. And now his horse was wandering away in search of a feed while he was banging at the rock with a pick. Suddenly Ed found what he was looking for. His pick didn't quiver in his hand as it struck the rock; its point plunged straight and firmly in. It was not rock; it was a kind of sticky clay. Hurriedly he hacked off the clay surface. Beneath was a long streak of silver, shining in the sun of that late afternoon.

Even the Indians could catch the glint of the seam as it

These ain't silver. These are rock . . . Git out of here

sparkled beneath them. They had never seen anything like it. Perhaps the paleface was some kind of god. They had better run back to tell Geronimo.

Ed pulled a 25-cent piece out of his pocket. Carefully he laid the piece down on top of the seam, then he placed his foot on top of it and pressed. He picked up the coin, and there beneath was a perfect impression of the engraving, for pure silver is soft.

"That'll larn Al Sieber!" Ed exclaimed. "I'll call this place Tombstone."

But striking silver and making it pay are two different things. Ed had to get into town, pick up food and more tools, register his claim, take on some men and generally set up business as a mine-owner. But for that he needed money; and all Ed had in the world was one ten-dollar bill and a twenty-five-cent coin.

Ed chipped off a few pieces of rock from near the seam. He wasn't going to take pure silver into town. "If the other prospectors catch sight of a lump of 'twinkle' they'd be off jumpin' this claim befire I can say 'Sprat'." Ed had no illusions. Nor did he intend to go into Bisbee. Chief Scout Sieber would soon be telling everyone how Ed had gone off into the San Pedro hills, so that by the time he got back these hills would be swarming with "desert rats". No, sir!

Ed got on to his horse and made for the little mining town of Signal. His brother Al worked there in the McCracken mine. Al was not half as keen to see Ed as Ed was to see him, which is not surprising, since after three weeks out in the desert Ed was the dirtiest, most down-at-heel miner that even shanty-town Signal had ever seen.

Ed kept his brother pinned down on his chair while he reeled off the tale of his lucky break. Al kept on trying to get up. He was due down at work. The whistle had gone. And hadn't he heard these tales a dozen times anyway? Usually he had to listen to these stories late at night; it was kind of unnatural to have this yarn poured out at eight o'clock of a morning before even Big Tony's saloon had opened its doors. But still, Brother Ed had always been a bit odd. He and his father had had to roam through half of Idaho looking for him when first he had run away from home on one of these gold-mining stunts.

"Ed," Al announced, "I jest ain't interested in rock. And

128

The postmaster raised his right hand and fired off his Colt

even if I was, I wouldn't lend you any dough to go wasting for me. Now, out of my way or you'll cost me my job."

Ed tried to interest some of the men in the saloon in the idea of lending him some money. But since most of Big Tony's patrons had the same sort of idea and very few of them had any money, he met with no success. At the dinner break Al told him bluntly that he was not going to keep him in food. If he wanted to eat, he would have to take a job down the mine. So, sinking his pride in an empty stomach, Ed lined up in front of the foreman's office and got himself taken on as pick-and-shovel man for McCracken.

After a couple of days Ed thought he would have a go at old McCracken. After all, there was no harm in trying.

McCracken sat at his desk. Ed swayed from one foot to the other as he tried to make his story sound probable.

"Show me the ore!" barked the mine boss.

Ed pulled his three chips from underneath his shirt. McCracken held them up in turn, turned them over, held them up to the light and then laid them down again.

"These ain't silver. These are rock. How come you waste my time like this? As if I ain't got something better to do than listen to every hoodlum who pushes in here to try and borrow a hundred dollars. Git out of here."

Ed grabbed his chippings and got out. Poor Ed! Life certainly played cruel tricks on a man. He could have made old McCracken's eyes pop out of his head, if he had cared to bring a lump of silver with him. These guys in Signal were just stupid, he reckoned. Why, anybody with a bit of know-how about mining would see that his chips could only have come from somewhere near the seam itself; they were high-grade silver ore, and he knew it.

"But guess there is one man in Signal," Ed mumbled to himself, "who ought to know a decent bit of ore when he's shown it." That was Richard Gird, the engineer of the McCracken mine. Ed went up to Gird on the workings and pulled him by his sleeve.

"Why not tell me here?" Gird grumbled. He was young, and he had no time to waste.

Ed explained that he might be overheard.

"Oh, very well, come into my office then."

5   129

Ed handed over his three precious chips. Gird promised to assay them.

"Look in here tomorrow evening just before you knock off, and I'll let you know how they make out under test."

"Say, thanks a lot!" Ed was certainly grateful. Gird was the first man who had shown the slightest interest since he had reached Signal.

On the next evening Gird was sitting waiting for Ed to knock on the door.

"Come in!" Ed was impatient too; he half-tripped over the step in the doorway.

"You know, Schiefflin, you've got something here."

"Sure I know. I've got a whizz-bang fortune."

"Steady-up! That's where you guys get me sick. Just because you knock off a piece of decent grade ore you think that you've come on a seam a foot thick."

"But I told you I *had*," Ed was insistent.

Gird revealed that one of the chips had assayed at two thousand dollars to the ton, another at six hundred and the third at only forty. Two thousand dollars a ton was good money, but it would only just pay back the expense of mining.

"Where's this lucky place of yours?" Gird inquired.

"Over yonder." Ed waved his hands towards the window. He wasn't going to let on to Gird or anyone else unless . . . And Gird was not going to lay out any money unless . . .

After a few days they struck a bargain. Gird would quit his job as McCracken's engineer and come with Ed, if he was allowed to cut in fifty-fifty.

As soon as Ed told him the news Al started to feel sorry—chiefly for himself.

"Didn't I always tell myself that there was something in those rocks, Ed? But I jest didn't want to encourage you too much. You know how it is, Ed."

"I know how it is now. And that's not thanks to you."

But Ed's heart was not much harder than pure silver. Yes, Al could come along too, and he could have a third share along with Gird and himself.

Ed led his brother and Richard Gird out into the San Pedro Hills straight to the spot where a month ago he had uncovered the seam of silver. He heaved a sigh of relief when he found that no one else had been chipping at it while he had been away in Signal. Ed never trusted any man when there was precious metal around; he had seen too many claims jumped.

Gird was not over-impressed with the silver seam. Ed could not make it out. But Gird had some Scots blood in his veins; he was cautious. Before he would commit himself he was going to find how deep the seam went.

"There's only three inches depth," he announced after his tests.

"Doggone it! Just my luck!" Ed had never thought of the possibility.

Al chipped in: "Can't see what you guys is worryin' about. Two inches, three inches. What's it matter? Why, it's worth a fortune." There was no putting off Al.

"I'm not worryin'," Gird answered. "This seam that Ed turned up must be an outspur of the main seam. We've got to start prospecting. The mother lode can't be far away."

"Aw, shucks!" Al spat out the baccy he was chewing. "Some guys never will be contented."

Al didn't have the prospector's spirit in him. He tried it, but soon got fed up with banging away day after day without success.

"I guess I wasn't made for this sort of thing," he declared one evening round the fire. "I don't mind working so long as I know what I'm a-doin'. Say, what about my diggin' out that load of silver Ed found?"

"No, you don't." Ed trusted his brother just about half an inch farther than other men, which was half an inch farther than no way at all. "When we comes to that, we all three dig, and we split in three shares. If you want to quit prospectin' you can do the cookin'. Dick and me could do with some decent grub, couldn't we?"

"Sure thing," Dick Gird agreed.

So it was settled that Al would do the cooking. Gird spent most of his time assaying the lumps of rock that Ed brought in. There was no stopping Ed; twice a day he would dump a sackful of chips down by Gird. It became a kind of routine as the days passed. But they were growing despondent. Though some of the chips proved good quality, none of them were spectacular.

Then one dinner hour Ed came running up, panting.

"Boys," he said, "I've hit the mother lode. She's all jake now."

"Zat so?" remarked Al, putting down the stew-pot. "You always was a lucky cuss."

"Lucky cuss! Sure, that's me! Guess I'll call the strike the 'Lucky Cuss Mine'." Ed was jumping with excitement.

Ed's sample assayed at fifteen thousand dollars a ton. It was the richest silver strike in the history of the west. He had made history. Within a couple of months the barren rockface was swarming with miners taken on to excavate the Lucky Cuss Mine. And in six months' time Ed was one of the richest men in America.

Gird took charge of the workings. Al had a special office building for himself, with "Mr. Al Schiefflin" painted in gold letters on the door. Inside, he spent his time counting through the piles of bank-notes. That was the steady sort of work that appealed to Al.

But Ed was nowhere to be seen round the Gird-Schiefflin Company's mine. He was back on his favourite hobby, collecting rocks.

Occasionally, well after nightfall, when there was no one else round the workings, Ed would creep in with his bag of chippings to take to Gird to have them assayed.

"Look here, Ed," Dick Gird said one evening. "Why don't you lay off this prospectin' business? You're rich. There ain't no need for you to work. Why, if you fancied it, you could just sit around all day in a fancy-pantsy office like brother Al, just counting through the piles of your dough."

"I'm not quittin', Dick." There was a sound of disappointment in Ed's voice: Gird should have known him better than to think that he would ever become an arm-chair boss. "Didn't you say that a seam like the Lucky Cuss had more than one outspur?"

Gird nodded his head.

"Well, I'm not layin' off until I've turned up every outspur that the old lady's got."

Gird pointed out that the job was not so easy as when they had first come into the San Pedro Hills. It had proved impossible to keep away the hundreds of lone-wolf prospectors who had come flocking in after the news of the Lucky Cuss strike. The "desert rats" were digging away over the ground for miles around. Ed only stood one chance in a thousand now.

132

"Those boys have got no patience." Ed knew his own strong point.

Ed carried on week after week. Then, just by a streak of his freakish luck, he came on an even bigger seam than the Lucky Cuss. It proved to be worth 75 million dollars. Ed called it the Tough Nut; it *had* certainly taken him a long time to find.

It was not long before Tombstone became the most famous mining city in the west. Every miner who could swing a pick made his way there; every saloon keeper, card-sharper, crook and bully showed up on Tombstone's main street. Within another year, by 1879, the empty stretch of the San Pedro Hills was covered with lines of huts, tents, shacks and even quite a few two-storey dwellings. The city counted more than ten thousand inhabitants; it had ten banks, fifteen barbers' saloons and more than a hundred saloons of the other kind. Wyatt Earp had been made Sheriff; every morning boys ran down Main Street with bundles of copies, still wet with printer's ink, of the city's own newspaper, the *Tombstone Epitaph*. Three thousand miles away on New York's Wall Street top-hatted bankers and stockbrokers pored over each issue of the *Epitaph* brought in by the mails. Every report of production from the Gird-Schieefflin mines sent the price of silver soaring to a new peak.

Al said good-bye to Arizona with a million dollars in his luggage. He was going to enjoy the high-spots. He reckoned that Gird could fit in time to count the bank-notes along with the rest of his duties.

As for Ed, fortune made no difference to him. They made him Mayor of the city, they hung pictures of him in every saloon, but they could not stop him digging. He would take no interest in the working of his mines, or in the money which they earned for him.

"Gird's the man for that," he would tell the folk that clustered round him when he stood at the bar. "I never was no good at keeping still."

"We heard you was a cavalry man once," someone said.

"Yeah." Ed swallowed a draught of his favourite beer. "I guess I chose the wrong service. I ought to have gone into one of those trench-digging outfits." The whole saloon shook with laughter: the figure of Ed swinging a pick had been adopted as the city's coat of arms.

One day Ed went into Gird's office to find a crowd of people in the room. "There he is," they shouted. "You ask him," they said to Gird. "Yes, go on!" Gird was none too keen on being the spokesman, because he had a fair idea of what Ed would reply, but he agreed reluctantly.

"It's like this, Ed," Gird explained. "The boys reckon that silver's pretty valuable."

"Sure thing!" Ed nodded. "It don't need any speechifyin' to tell me that."

"But they reckon that it would be even more valuable if Uncle Sam made silver the official currency instead of gold. And they think that you ought to go up to Washington and tell the President so."

"Why me?" Ed did not like the sound of the proposition.

"Because you are the Mayor of Tombstone."

"When you asked me to be Mayor, you said the job didn't mean no work 'cept wearin' a chain round my neck."

"All right, Ed, don't go as Mayor." Dick was placating. "Tell the President that the man who founded Tombstone wants to see him."

It took three hours of persuading to get Ed to go. He had never been near a city—not since the age of five when his parents had stopped one night in Chicago on the trek west from Ohio to Wyoming. What he had heard tell did not make him feel any great wish to go.

Ed's send-off was a great event in Tombstone. Beforehand the boys had sent away to St. Louis to fetch the best outfit that money could buy for Ed. They dressed him up in a silk hat and morning coat. On his feet they slipped a pair of the latest patent leather boots. Then came the great moment when the stage-coach was due to start. The brass band struck up "Hurrah, the conquering hero comes", the crowd waved their caps in the air and shouted "Strike lucky, Ed!"

Ed arrived in Washington to find that he was famous. As soon as he stepped out of the railway car the news reporters were on to him.

"Is it true that you're worth five million, Mr. Schiefflin?"

"Would you favour our readers with your views on bimetallism?"

"Say, Mr. Schiefflin, what do you think about the Anglo-French tension in the Sudan?"

"Lookey-here!" Ed was getting flustered for just about the first time in his life. "There ain't no good askin' me about nothin'. I ain't got no book learnin'. Now if you was to show me some lumps of rock, I could tell you a thing about them. F'rinstance, I've got a trunk full of rocks loaded on that train."

Next morning the newspapers announced that "Lucky" Ed Schiefflin had brought a collection of gold and silver ores to present to the nation. For a whole week the papers seemed to carry no other story except those about Ed. The President asked him to dinner, the French Ambassador gave a reception in his honour; several senators invited him to stay on their country estates.

Ed was longing to get back to Tombstone, or anywhere where he could get digging again. But for Ed there was to be a new kind of gold-digging. Charities were hot on his tail; there were mountains of begging letters by every post. He was virtually kidnapped and taken to New York to be the guest of honour at a dinner in aid of an orphanage. This time he was the gold, and someone else did the digging.

Yet he could not go back just for a while. The Senate was going to consider the whole question of silver currency at its next session. He had been invited to give evidence before one of its committees. In the end it took him a whole year to pull himself clear; by then he had been tamed. A young lady had dug her way into his heart, and now he did not want to go back to Tombstone, because the young lady said that Tombstone was no place for nice girls.

"Still, you can't force me to stay east, Mary," Ed was more plaintive than defiant. "My folks moved west when they was young. There's air out there—a man can breathe; its stifling in these cities."

"But, Ed, you promised!" Mary could not help smiling, and the corners of her rounded mouth twisted ever so slightly.

"Yeah, I know I said I wouldn't go back to Tombstone, but there's more of the West than Tombstone or Bisbee or even the whole of Arizony. Now what about you and me compromisin'? We could go out to 'Frisco and build ourselves a nice house outside the city on the shores of the rolling Pacific. You'd be near a city, and I'd be in the West. What about it?"

And so it was settled that they should live in San Francisco. Ed built the house just as he promised, but life did not turn out as he hoped. Once a prospector, always a prospector. Now that he had got money, he sat dreaming on the veranda overlooking the ocean of how he might fit out an expedition to sail in search of gold in foreign parts.

Mary realized that there was no stopping him. Together with Ed she helped to design the steamboat that was to take him up to the frozen seas of Alaska. She went down to the harbour mouth to wave as the ship turned its head north from the Golden Gate towards the great expanse of snow-capped rock which Uncle Sam had recently bought from the Russians.

Ed was gone nearly a year. When he got back he was full of talk about the possibilities of finding gold up north. The place fairly smelled of gold, he declared.

"If only I could spend a year or two getting down to real diggin'. Why, I didn't have time to do more than look round!"

"But, Ed." If he had noticed, he would have seen the tears in Mary's eyes. "This is your home. I'm the girl you married. Surely you're not going to leave us just as soon as you're back."

Ed gave in. Mary had laid out a fine garden for him while he was away. She told him that he could dig that to his heart's content, if he wanted digging. And Mary was not only a sweet girl; she was also a shrewd one. She had had the gardeners bury little pieces of queer-coloured rock beneath the beds, so that every now and then Ed would come running up to her as she sat embroidering, shouting: "Do you know what, Mary dear? I guess this house is built right on top of a seam of precious metal!"

But the time came when Ed had excavated the last of the coloured rocks, and Mary noticed the change in him. He would pace up and down the veranda.

"Ed, for goodness' sake come and sit down. You give me nerves; you're so restless. What's biting you?" Mary lay down her embroidery.

"I was just a-thinkin'," Ed explained.

"Thinking of where you could go next, I suppose."

"It's kind of like that, Mary. You see, there's talk of gold

136

being found in Oregon, and I reckon that if there's gold about I'm the one to look for it."

"But aren't you rich enough, Ed?"

"Sure, sure. But it's not like that. It's something inside of me that makes me want to dig."

"Well, I suppose I'll have to let you go, Ed Schiefflin. You'll give me no peace if I say no."

So it was that in January 1897 he put off his respectable city clothes and got into his miner's kit once more. This time he would take no expedition with him. He reckoned that he had been wrong to go to Alaska with such a crowd of assistants. When a man's looking for gold, he said, he had best be by himself. "There's only a certain amount of luck to go round; if there's too many after it, no one gets any worth speaking about. It's each man for himself, when it comes to prospecting."

Ed set out alone for Douglas County, Oregon. Every week he settled down to write Mary a letter; though he was no scholar, he liked to describe to her the quality of the various pieces of rock which he had collected. After a while his letters became more enthusiastic. One of them read: "I have found stuff here in Oregon which will make Tombstone look like salt. This is GOLD." Another enclosed a rough-drawn map of the North Umpqua country with two places marked by a cross and the word "here" written by the side.

Mary passed on the news to her friends in San Francisco, and soon it leaked to the newspapers.

RICHER THAN TOMBSTONE
"Lucky" Ed strikes gold in Oregon

the headlines proclaimed. Men packed up their kit and started north to find fortune in Oregon's woods. Another gold rush was under way. Then one morning the papers appeared with a different headline:

"LUCKY" ED FOUND DEAD
Foul play suspected.

But there had been no foul play. Ed was no longer the youngster he used to be: digging all day had proved too much for

137

him. He had had a heart attack when he reached his cabin; he had fallen down on the floor while lighting his pipe.

They are still looking for the fabulous strike which Ed announced in his letters home. For fifty years the search has gone on in vain. It seems that Ed took the secret with him to the next world.

His body they took to Tombstone, and there they buried it in style fitting for the founder of the richest, wildest, wickedest city on the face of the earth. Today Tombstone is nothing more than a village. The mines are worked out, the miners have gone. The people who remain are caretakers of a city of ruins. But "Lucky" Ed's spirit still hovers round the San Pedro Hills, wishing good luck to the stray "hard-timer" digging away with his pick, looking for the seam that all the others missed.

As for Ed, it's a fair bet that he is still digging wherever he is. And who knows? He might be in a place where it is supposed to be all gold.

THE GHOST THAT CAME EAST

This is a story about the Wild West of America, about the time when it was at its wildest. Strangely, you may think, it is told in a café-bar down by the waterside in Paris. But then it is a strange story. And the oddest thing of all is that I am alive to tell it.

I'll not trouble you much with a description of me. As I look at myself in the streaked mirror over there, I can hardly guess that the fellow I am looking at is the self-same man whose red hair once blew across a fresh-skinned face, a face that all the ladies said was pretty good-looking. Now the hair—what is left of it—is white; and there is a dark scar running across the left cheek. But I will not tell more about what I can see in that mirror. It is not a pretty sight.

You will be wondering why I, a full-blooded American born and bred in the Illinois woods, should be sitting cocking an eye at my ugly mug in the mirror, here in a low-down bar in Paris. You will be wondering a lot of things before this story is through. But I guess that I had better answer your first question. I am not here because I want to be, or because I like it. I am here because there is no place left in my own country to go. I am here because it is safe, because they won't find me here. And, if they did run this old fox to earth, somehow I guess they would not connect that haggard face in the mirror with the man for whom they were looking.

So, you see, this place is kind of strange to me. I don't know the lingo, and I am too old a dog to learn new tricks. All that's familiar is the taste of the Scotch that they keep for me in a bottle on the counter. I like the way it burns a hole right down my middle. I like its rough taste. There are times when I put my hand down to my side to feel for the flask that I always used to carry in the pocket of my riding breeches. But it is not there now. I lost that flask the time I had to leave St. Louis on the run. The only way to safety that night was to step into a tailor's shop, try on a new kit, overcoat and hat; and then skip out again with my hat brim well down over my eyes. It did the trick. They ought to have known that you can always tell a man

139

by his gait; but they were raw—quick on the trigger, but that was about all. Anyhow I left that flask in my old breeches; and I have never felt like getting myself another.

That old flask had got a couple of dents in its side: each one of those was the mark of a slug that had cut through the leather outer skin before coming up with a bump against the steel lining. Strong steel that was; made in Pennsylvania by an old Scots pal of mine. He said the time would come when the flask would save my life. He said that with a great guffaw of a laugh, but I guess he did not mean it in the way that turned out. He knew that I spent most of the day in the saddle, often as not riding across those waterless wastes of Arizona and New Mexico. What he did not know was that, though water in those parts was scarcer than gold dust, there was nothing deserted about those deserts.

Every crazy-shaped rock across the sandy plains might have had a man with a gun behind it; often did. The first slug that plunged into that flask came from nowhere. I was riding along beside my stage-coach—that was my job, running coaches— when there was a long low whistle like the north wind coming down a gully. And then before I could look up to see from where it was coming I was holding for grim life on to my reins, lying flat over the saddle. That slug packed a fair-sized punch. There wasn't a soul in sight beyond my own lads riding on the coach which was carrying a load of nuns to the San Antonio Mission. Gunmen dressed up in nun's outfits were not unheard of in the west of America, but that shot could not have come from the coach. I had checked up on each one of those nuns myself before selling them a ticket. I had had a good look at their feet. You can always tell a man from a woman by his feet no matter what silky clothes he may be wearing.

There was nothing else moving in that desert except our horses rearing their forelegs as if someone was tugging on their tails. Horses have a kind of sixth sense to warn them and their riders of danger. The hot air shimmered over the scalding sand like the steam gathering over the spout of a kettle. But nothing moved, not the spikes of the prickly pears, not the vulture perched on its topmost branch.

I knew who had fired that shot. I knew his name, his face, his walk, the scar down his back and the way he held a cigar up to his mouth between two dainty fingers. That last was the reason why they called him "Mary" O'Callaghan out West. "Mary" used to belong to my outfit. I had hired him for good wages, paid him danger money on "bullion rides", given him my own bedding roll when his got carried away while fording a flooded river. But someone had paid him better. And "Mary" just could not resist the crackling sound of new greenbacks.

Black Rourke had paid him a playing-card pack of $50 bills in return for the tip-off when my coach was plying from Sacramento across to Denver with a load of bullion. I had become suspicious as soon as I saw "Mary" playing poker for 50-dollar stakes the first night we made camp. Betting that high wasn't healthy for him or for me. I didn't know nothing: I just had a few ideas swimming round the back of my head. Rourke had held up my coaches before. He had not struck bullion, but he had picked up a tidy collection of gold objects dropped in a hurry by my passengers. One of these days he would score a bull's-eye and hit the "Bullion Express".

Come nightfall I didn't waste longer than it took me to circle the camp and check that all the horses were safely tethered. Fifty miles away or so on the Northern Trail one of my coaches should be plying east: or rather at this time of night the crew and passengers would be bedded down round a blazing fire. If I got up on the saddle and rode like the west wind itself I could make that camp, do what I wanted and still be back lying doggo underneath my blanket by the time that "Mary" opened his blinking eyes and peered at the dawn.

You can probably guess how I had figured out things. It all planned out just like you thought and I hoped. I got back before anyone noticed that I'd gone. "Mary" might have spotted that the bay mare I was riding the next day wasn't the same bay as I had been jogging along the day before, but he didn't. The Northern Trail coach switched off its old track, careered up and down the hills that lay in the direction of the Southern Trail. Meanwhile I kept the boys on the "Bullion Express" moving slowly as if they were pulling a load of fresh chickens' eggs instead of something as unbreakable as fifty gold ingots. They didn't care much: riding quietly gave them a chance to take a few pot-shots at the bird life of those parts.

The other coach dodged on to the Southern Trail not more

than ten miles in front of the "Bullion Express". I could just see the dust cloud if I peered hard. Of course, I wasn't sure that anything would happen, or if it did happen, where or when it might be. The gang-men have a mountain of an advantage over the coaches: they can pick and choose their ambush. Not difficult doing: every mile of that drive had a spur of rock or overhanging cliff. All I could do was to keep that cloud of dust just at the limit of my vision.

Next day there was no mistaking the sound: no one was taking a shot at a covey of birds. Those shots were fired in anger. "Right, boys," I cried, "here is where we get into action. Unleash that coach and follow me." I knew that my lads on the other coach would not have been caught napping. Still they could not be expected to hold out for ever. The passengers would panic. I had told the coachman to tell his passengers to lie flat on the floor of the coach when shooting started. I did not want Rourke to discover that he had held up the wrong coach before strictly necessary.

We covered those ten miles as quick as horseflesh will go. I just had time to wonder how "Mary" was feeling, and to notice that he was keeping well up with the bunch. Then we were coming round the bend of the trail, blazing for all we were worth. Rourke's boys must have felt pretty miserable caught between our fire and that from the lads on the coach. They kept their end up for a minute, and then Rourke gave the word to those that were left. Off they rode. They galloped up to the hills from where they had come. And then it was that Rourke must have given another order. A volley came out from behind those rocks—ten guns firing as one—and all those bullets were aimed at one man. That man was "Mary" O'Callaghan. He had double-crossed them; that was what they thought. And there is only one pay-off out West for a double-crosser. As fate would have it, "Mary" didn't peg out. He lay on the dust with a hole like the entrance to a rabbit warren in his back. But my men patched him up and kept him going on Scotch; and I didn't stop them. I could have done so easily, but I didn't.

The trouble with the West is that no man gives another credit for a single decent motive. Rourke made up his mind that "Mary" had been playing a double game. "Mary" decided that he had been made the victim of a "frame-up", that I had put

Rourke up to the stunt of offering him dollars just to squeeze him into the tight hole that ended with a bullet lodged in his spinal cord—an elaborate way of getting rid of a rival. Shucks! "Mary" was no rival of mine. He might have been quick on the draw, but he hadn't got what it takes to run a string of stage-coaches. As for elbowing me out of the head of the outfit, he could no more have done that than take over from the President himself. He was a second-rater. And like all second-raters he nursed a grouse until it became bigger than himself.

"Mary" could not exactly go to join Rourke, and his reputation wasn't so sweet that he would have been welcomed by any other mob. As soon as he could get on the saddle again he quit my outfit. He left word to tell me that he had sworn on the book not to gamble or drink the spirits until he had got even with a certain person whose identity was quite well known to me.

The strange thing about it was that he managed to keep so long on the water wagon. At first, waiting for a knife in the dark or a bullet out of the blue got on my nerves. Then I reckoned that "Mary" could never keep away from the bottle that long, so I put him out of my mind. After all, he wasn't the first rider of mine who had gone off threatening murder. But as soon as I felt that bullet dig into my flask, and even before I had time to thank whoever keeps the Big Book up top I knew it was "Mary" who had fired that gun, as sure as if his signature had been written on the bullet.

I knew he had fired it, and I knew he was skulking out there behind one of those rocks with his gun cocked a second time, with his sights up to his eyes—waiting.

There are times in a man's life when he just doesn't know what makes him do something. I guess that the old fellow who ticks off the names in the Big Book sticks his finger in the works some place. Anyhow, before I knew what I was doing, I was up in that saddle, standing in my stirrups yelling.

"Mary, you dirty swine!" I yelled. "Your bullets are dud. You thought of everything, didn't you, except the bullets. Well, they're phoney—I fixed that."

"Framer!" screamed "Mary" with a voice that made the horses rear again.

"Fire them off if you're too numb-skulled to believe!" I challenged him.

The numb-skull fell for it. He fired off round after round without sighting his Winchester properly, and they whistled wide. That was all I wanted. It gave me the chance to locate his hide-out from the muzzle flashes. My boys didn't wait for any orders. Their horses were off like greyhounds after raw meat. And "Mary" wasn't patched up this time. Any surgical operation that there was the vultures provided.

The second dent in my flask was about an inch away from the first. They looked like twins and the relationship wasn't coincidental. But I am going to have Madame bring me another swig from my Scotch bottle before I get round to tracing the connection. Bless me! The spirit still does something to me. As it drops down my throat for a couple of seconds, I get that feeling of strength into my old bones, the same as I had in the far-away days when I was the ace of stage-coach men, when Wells, Fargo was just a "one-horse" show with a couple of coaches and I ruled the western trails.

"Mary" hadn't wasted the days between leaving my outfit and my leaving him with a body so riddled that it wouldn't have been used as a sieve. He had been passing rather more than the time of day with my best customers, the California Bank manager, the bosses of the Western Star Bank and the gang of crooks who called themselves the Grand National Bank.

"Mary" had been spinning these gentlemen a nice little yarn. By the time he had got through with it they were jumping mad. And I don't blame them. "Mary" had come along to explain to them how I had been robbing them systematically over the years. According to him I had got a regular factory out in the Nevada desert, tucked away in a cavern. My bullion coaches, so he yarned, would come lumbering up to this cavern, spill out a load of gold blocks, take on another similar load and then drive off again. The point was that the second load of blocks were lead, plated with a thin veneer of gold. Not a bad dodge!

It wouldn't have been too hard to manage either. Only someone would have found out soon enough, if I had been playing that sort of game, without waiting for "Mary" to come along and squeal. Most of the blocks were shipped back east and stored in the bullion rooms of the great banks, but sooner or later someone would have melted down a block and then his eyes would have popped out. One of the bank stiff-collars asked "Mary" about that.

"Surely, we'd have had complaints, Mr. O'Callaghan?" he said.

"Not necessarily, Mr. Morgenstern," "Mary" squirmed like a sardine trying to get out of the net. "You see that operator is devilish cunning. Not all the substituted blocks are phoneys. Just one or two, here and there."

The worst of it was that I had got just such a cavern near the salt desert as "Mary" described. It was common knowledge throughout the West that I had a number of posting stations of my own, places where my coaches could change their horses and where the passengers could get out to have a wash. The most famous of these joints was the cavern at the edge of the salt desert. Coaches coming in from the forty-miles run across the salt had horse teams that were just about dropping for want of water. Going the other way we used to load up the passengers with water bottles before the coaches left for the desert trip. It was in that cavern that I did store gold. It wasn't my gold; it belonged to my customers.

In those roaring days most of the banks were about as safe as a house without a door. A guy would arrive in town one evening, have himself a wooden shanty run up, and then a couple of days later he would nail up a board proclaiming the "New World Bank" or some such glorious name. Sometimes the manager was on the level. But more often than not he was just "one of the boys". What he took in over the counter he passed out through the back door. Even the straight ones found it hard to make a go. They were always being asked for loans, and then when the bloke whose money they were lending came to ask for it back, they had to beg pardon and ask for time.

Not surprising that many folk weren't going to put their money in any bank. Knowing me as a fellow who transported gold all over the West, they would ask me if I knew somewhere safe where they could put away their savings. It was then that my thoughts had turned to the cavern by the desert. The hole was immense. You would never guess so from the entrance which wasn't any larger than the double-door of a saloon. But inside —why, it was as large as that cathedral they've got on the island

145

here in Paris. Wouldn't be amazed if the whole island would
have gone into the cave as well.

Not a bad place for a hide-away, eh? That was what I
reckoned. I didn't tell my customers just where it was I would
keep their gold, but I gave them to understand that the where-
abouts were just about as safe as the Bank of England and the
Rock of Gibraltar rolled into one. And I gave as good as my
word. I had a dozen men with guns stationed outside that
cavern mouth. And there wasn't a time of day or night when
a lad wouldn't be pacing up and down on sentry-go.

So, when "Mary" told these bank gentlemen that I've got a
plant for changing gold into lead stored away in that cavern,
they raised their hands in saintly horror.

"Now, we know," they say, "why he keeps a garrison out
there in the desert. Would be kind of awkward if he had some
nosey visitors, wouldn't it?"

I don't know just what happened or how the wretch got
inside. All I know is that one fine day when I'm sitting up on
the seat of the Santa Fe Express, flicking the whip lazily over
the horses' backs a messenger rides up as fast as if the hooves of
his beast are on fire.

"Boss," he shouts, "they're wanting you back at Fresh
Cavern. Some squirt's been smelling around in there."

"Just you wait till I get my hands around his neck," says I,
leaping off the seat. "I'll get on Lucky and ride back with you."
Lucky was my favourite horse: I kept her trailing behind the
coach whenever I was driving.

The squirt had the laugh on me. I rode flat out for sixteen
hours, till Lucky was near to dropping. All the while I was going
through in my mind who it might be who had sent that nosey-
parker sniffing round Fresh Cavern. I had worked out a few
searching questions to ask the long nose. But he was not there
to be asked anything.

"Just slipped away, Boss," my boys said, shrugging their
shoulders. "We tied him up, but guess he must have wriggled
out somehow. We didn't spot it till Mike looked in with his
breakfast and then he weren't there. Sure, we're very sorry,
Boss."

There were quite a few things I might have said just then. But
it doesn't do for a man always to say what is on his mind. Slip

out, my gouty foot! Someone let that guy out. And that some-one was still around here. Just wait till I caught him.

"Guess it can't be helped," I said. "Come on, give Lucky a drink and some oats. She's tired and so am I. Guess I could do with some oats too."

It wasn't safe for a man who controls a great enterprise like my Adams Express Company to quit doing the rounds inspect-ing the outfit. I might have thought of that when I was hanging round Fresh Cavern, but I didn't. I couldn't get it out of my mind that among those "yes-sir", "no-sir", slap-happy boys of mine was one galut who was two-faced. So, I would hang around the camp fire of an evening with my ears hanging down like a spaniel. When a coach came in with mail I would take all the letters for the boys into my office, lock the door and steam open the envelopes.

Of course, I didn't know then about the tale that "Mary" had spilled out on those bankers' desks. It was a puzzle to me who could have sent that snooper. I knew "Mary" was lying out there on the sand feeding the vultures and the mountain lions: it wasn't like Black Rourke to use sly methods—he was a coach-robber, and coach-robbers fight fair according to their fashion. I reckoned that Wells, Fargo were at the back of it.

The first gold had been panned in California three years before the local rag, the *Alta California*, carried a notice to say that the New York merchants had formed the Wells, Fargo company to run stage expresses to and from the goldfields. In due course a bunch of Easterners came round the Horn and set up shop in San Francisco. At that time my company controlled most of the stage routes of the West. There were a few indepen-dent operators; I didn't care about them much. Come to think of it, it isn't healthy for one outfit to have no competition—so I didn't interfere much with the smaller fry.

Wells, Fargo started off in a modest way with a couple of coaches. After a while I didn't pay much attention to them. They wouldn't have been the first bunch of New Yorkers who had come out West shouting too loud. Then it got round to me that Mr. Wells had been quietly buying up the other independent operators. He hadn't been changing the names on the outside of their coaches, but he owned them all right, lock, stock and barrel. Within a couple of years Wells, Fargo were a power in

California. They were running a regular banking business; they were acting as shipping agents for most of the goods that were brought into the West and for most of the gold that was sent out on the ocean clippers.

It didn't need a clairvoyant to see that I was in the way of Messrs. Wells, Fargo. As a matter of a fact a banker friend of mine had hinted one day that Wells was prepared to pay me a nice round heap of dollars to clear out. I'd been pretty rude about that offer: sent to tell Mr. Wells that I'd see him in Kamkatchka before I quit the stage-coaching game. Since then Mr. Wells and I weren't on speaking terms, though we were playing poker together with the whole of California's transportation as the stake.

Yes, it wasn't beyond the bound of any possibilities that Wells, Fargo were at the bottom of this: they had plenty of dough to spare, and it looked as if some of it was trickling into the pockets of the boys I hired to guard Fresh Cavern. I didn't like the look of it. The more I hung round the cave eavesdropping, the less I liked it. But there was nothing to be done. No other snooper turned up. There was no attack. None of my boys quit.

After a month I threw in my hand.

"I'm going back on the trail, boys," I said. "Guess you must be feeling pretty lonely up here by the desert. No pretty ladies to dance with. Tell you what I'll do. I'll send back some of the other boys to relieve you, and you can take a turn on the coaches."

"Don't worry about us, Boss!" they said, with a half-smile stealing over their faces.

"Curse their guts!" I said to myself. "No wonder they don't want to quit Fresh Cavern. They are getting paid by me to guard the cave, and paid by someone else to split on what is being put inside. The sooner I get some of the boys I can trust up here, the better for yours faithfully, Harry Shemayne Adams." And I dug my spurs into Lucky so hard that she jumped into the air.

When I started on the rounds again I noticed a lot of new faces.

"Who are these guys?" I asked.

"Had to hire 'em, Boss," the coach chiefs told me. Several of the boys had gone sick; others had quit to try a hand pegging out a gold claim on one of the new fields. I looked the recruits over: they didn't seem the picture of health themselves. Hangdog faces, twisted grins, hook hands and gammy legs. A rare crew, I said to myself.

Hang on for a minute while I light this cheroot. That's a shade better. Feels more like old times with a cigar a-puffing between my lips. Would you care for one yourself? No, I guess not. They're on the strong side, I'll agree. But we got in the habit of smoking uncured baccy in those western days.

As I was saying, I went the rounds of my empire, travelling with each coach in turn, checking its time and its pay-load, pi-jawing with the agents at the passenger offices, inspecting the horses at the posting stations.

It was about at this time that the U.S. Postmaster put out for tenders to carry Uncle Sam's mails. Before then there had been no official post: anyone with a letter sent it down to the stage-coach office, paid freight, and the coach chief handed it over to the office at the other end of the ride, where it had to be collected.

Uncle Sam was willing to pay quite generously the outfit which carried the mail; and—what was equally important—he was prepared to protect mail coaches with cavalry men over runs infested with robbers. Naturally Wells, Fargo and I both put in a tender. And—an old Wild West custom—we both slipped a little green-backed reminder to the clerks working in the new post office. The clerks pocketed the bills from each of us without the least trace of favouritism. Then the Postmaster came out with an announcement that, in order to choose fairly, he would give the mail contract to the coaching company whose coach covered the ground between San Francisco and Los Angeles in the shortest time.

The whole of San Francisco fashion—bankers with fur round their collars, ladies of the town with fur round their ankles—turned out to see the start of the coach race. I was mounted on the driving seat with a long whip in each hand and a brand-new fawn felt topper on my head. A cheroot was hanging out of the corner of my mouth just as it is now. All my boys were dressed in blue coats with yellow facings. Wells, Fargo's outfit had coachmen clad in green, like the colour of the iron shutters that hang by the windows of all their offices. Each coach had a hornsman blowing away for all he was worth. The little boys in the audience clapped and shouted, the ladies fanned themselves. The Postmaster raised his right hand and fired off his Colt. The two coaches lurched forwards—the race was on.

As luck would turn out, we hadn't got more than twenty miles outside town when a wheel came toppling off. The coach rolled over and all the mail spilled on the dust. I had checked over the coach that very morning, but I hadn't noticed anything queer about that wheel.

"Heave her up, boys," I shouted, dusting down my pants after the throw.

But the boys were a ham-handed lot. They let the coach drop. They couldn't find the spare peg to hold the wheel. All the while the Wells, Fargo crew were forging farther ahead. I looked up and couldn't even see the dust that they had kicked up—it had all settled.

I was boiling inside by the time the wheel was fixed again. What a raw crew! I ought to have picked a better lot. Down went my whips and off went the coach. Didn't I just crack those horses along. They couldn't make out what was hitting them, I guess. But did they pull? They weren't just four ordinary horses: they were English thoroughbreds.

I rode those horses until the sweat was running off their flanks in little waterfalls. At the posting station I had another team of thoroughbreds waiting. Late that evening we came to a river. Way upstream was a ford; it meant a detour of several miles to go round by the ford. I was willing to bet my bottom dollar that the Wells-Fargo outfit would go round that way. And I was willing to risk that same dollar on crossing the river straight. I'd done it before, though never in such a tearing hurry as on this night.

I had the coach lifted off the wheels. Each horse had a wheel tied round its girth, lying over the saddle; and then I led them into the water. They swam as if they had been born to it. That left the coach. Back I went to fetch it. Down we lowered the box into the water. We pushed it out into the water and swam like fury behind it. It wasn't exactly watertight, but we got it across before it capsized.

There was no time for anyone to dry themself. On went the wheels and off we raced. The crew weren't too happy. We struck the trail going round by the ford after about two miles. I was as pleased as punch: we came on to that road just a hundred yards ahead of the Wells, Fargo coach. I let out a whelping cheer, but the boys kept their mouths closed.

All through the night we kept gaining on the other coach. Daybreak found us a mile ahead and only three hours out from Los Angeles. With any decent luck we would come in comfortably first.

As it happened, it wasn't luck that kept us back from winning that race.

"Brake's jammed, Boss," one of the boys shouted.

He didn't need have shouted. I could feel it; I could hear the shrill whine of the brake shoe rubbing against the wheel.

"Get the —— thing loose!" I yelled back.

"Can't, Boss," the brakeman replied.

"Jumping cats!" I pulled tight on the reins to bring the horses in. The guy was right. The brake had come right off its screw. There was no use winding away; nothing happened. I jumped down to have a good look. The shoe had got twisted in some way that I'd never seen in a dozen years of coaching.

"We'll have to take the whole thing down," I cried. "Come on, lads. Get out the tools."

One didn't have to be a detective to reckon what was going on. A couple of the boys, two of the vilest rapscallions I've caught sight of, became sick of the palsy, as the Book puts it. Couldn't lift a thing; couldn't find the tools; couldn't understand what was being said to them. Plain dumb they acted.

It was as plain as the sight of the Wells, Fargo coach thundering by as we were stuck there yelling sweet epithets at each other: it was plain that those two guys knew quite a bit about how that brake shoe came to be twisted.

I brought out my gun on them. "I know your type of rat!" I shouted. "Get your backs facing me. Now scram just as fast as your smelly feet will carry you, or I'll tickle your backsides with some '45 shot."

They went. Like lizards disturbed from an afternoon doze, one moment they were there, next they were gone.

We had the brake off in a few minutes. It would have been hopeless to try to fix it on again: our only hope was to move off as quick as we could, brake or no brake. I drove those horses until they seemed to neigh back, "No more! No more!" I drove them until we got back in sight of the Wells, Fargo coach. But we hadn't a dog's chance. Their lead was too great. They rolled into the little village of the Angels a good twenty lengths ahead. And that's how I lost the mails' contract to Wells, Fargo.

I'm not saying just who hired those two dagoes to unfix my wheel and to jam my brake, because I haven't any definite proof. But I've sure got suspicions. It doesn't do, as I was saying before, to lay off doing the rounds inspecting the coaches and the routes. While I was hanging about Fresh Cavern, my competitors had the field clear to plant their men in my crews.

The Mayor of Los Angeles put a wreath of flowers around my head. "The loser's prize," he called it. I wasn't exactly in the mood to smile. I muttered thanks to the old swell-belly and wandered off towards the boss of the Fargo crew. There was some reckoning up to be done.

The Wells, Fargo boss took a step towards me.

"Mr. Adams, suh," he says in a Southern drawl that grated on my backbone, "you sure got some fine horses there."

"So what?" I snarled.

"Would you be caring to sell out now?" He rolled each word round his mouth.

For answer to that I planted my left straight on the point of his chin. There was the deuce of a shindy. The boys in each crew started laying into each other. The poor little Mayor danced round as if he had got ants in his pants. Finally he gives the word and the municipal fire wagon crew started pumping water straight into us.

Ever tried to stand up against a hose jet of water? Well, don't! Walking on a soapy floor is easy compared with that. We all tumbled over on top of each other in a sodden heap. Lucky, as we were so hot from the ride that none of us minded the showerbath.

I got up and swept my hand over my wet hair and walked over to the local postmaster.

"Does that mean that Wells, Fargo get the contract?" I inquired.

"That's how it would seem, Mr. Adams," the guy replied, swaying around on his heels.

"Then I'm going to put a stop to this dirty work!" I said, feeling for the butt in my holster.

"I wouldn't get across the path of Uncle Sam, if I were you, Mr. Adams," he answers all suavely. And I go striding off.

From that day onwards my troubles came down as steadily as winter rain. Wells, Fargo became the "Number One" express company. With the mails' contract they opened offices in every town worth the name. Every time I caught sight of one of their notices "By appointment to U.S. Postmaster" I felt hot and cold in turn. But there was nothing to be done about it. I spilled my story to one of the State Senators; he offered me a cigar and told me not to be a bad loser. Wells, Fargo were on the up, and I was on the down; and that was all there was to it.

I started off on the trail again, determined to fire any man who looked as if he was playing a double game.

I just happened to be at Fresh Cavern when Black Rourke rode into the attack. He had the best part of twenty-five men, which was twice the number I could call on. We had the best of the position. I hadn't chosen the site of the hide-away in a half an hour. I had picked a gulley that could be defended by a few men squatting on top of the cliffs towering over its two sides. At the end of the gulley, at the mouth of the Salt Desert itself, stood the sentry.

I was brushing down Lucky, rubbing her with a rough towel, when the sentry's whistle sent a shiver down my spine. I had been waiting for that piercing sound for years, months, weeks, days: at last it had come. The boys knew what to do. Each one picked up his gun, slung a belt of bullets over his shoulder and started clambering up the walls of the gulley. Just Jake Kennedy and I stayed down by the mouth of the cave, a last-ditch resort.

Sure as we had reckoned, after putting a bullet through the sentry, Black Rourke's boys started heading up the gulley. Wasn't there half a cannonade waiting for them? I can hear the din even now. The gulley echoed with the smash of lead shots tearing home to their mark. Rourke's horses reared and panicked. The bolts of my boys' guns clicked backwards and forwards as if they were automatic.

"That's larned them," I said to Jake, fairly jumping with excitement.

"Hope they've got Rourke himself, Boss." Jake was scanning the view with a pair of field-glasses.

"The dirty skunk; I'll lay you a gold mine to a coco-nut that Rourke's been given the tip-off. This is way off his beat."

"Look, Boss!" Jake clutched my arm. He was pointing down the gulley. A body, as small as a doll it looked from where we were standing, was hurtling down from the cliff-top. Whump! It fell with a sickening thud. I started to run towards the accident when there's a great shriek from somewhere above me. Then a rattle of bullets cracks through the air, and Harry the hunchback rolls down the mountainside.

"Rourke's come round over the top." I shout at Jake as if he were some way to blame. "Blow that whistle long and hard. That'll call in the boys."

We had agreed this plan long ago. The boys on the opposite cliff came tearing down the rocks to join Jake and me. Not one of our lads on the cliff immediately above the cave turned up, so it looked as if Rourke's men commanded all those heights. It wouldn't be long before they were down in the valley ready to challenge us for mastery of the cave.

Without a moment to lose we got to work lugging boulders into the cave mouth. The boulders were all there waiting to be put into position to make a wall. Hadn't we practised the manœuvre often enough? But never had we worked so fast as we did on that afternoon.

We had just about got the wall up to shoulder height when Rourke appeared on the scene with over a dozen of his men. Evidently their reckless dash up the valley had cost him half his total force. We numbered seven.

"Get out of here, Rourke," I called out from behind the wall, "or your mother will never see you again."

Rourke slapped his hands on his hips and stuck his chin out like as if he were a conquering general.

"Adams," he snarls, "you can't bluff me with your threats. This time you're on the wrong side of the law, not me. You've got that cave full of stolen gold. Give over or we'll take it from you, you stage-coach hypocrite, you."

"There ain't no stolen gold here," I replied confidently. "And you can't fool me with that kind of talk. I tell you to clear out of this valley." And I raised my gun to the ready just to show that I meant business.

Rourke's lieutenant, a mulatto sailor boy, comes over to him and starts whispering down his ear. Rourke nods his head.

"Adams!" he calls.

"Yeah?" I says.

"If you can prove you ain't got no gold in that cave, I'll ride away and take my boys with me. Open up that wall and let's have a look inside. That's fair, ain't it?"

I smelled that rat before ever it was born. I wasn't pulling down that wall to please Mr. Black Rourke.

"Who sent you, Rourke?"

"What's that to you, hypocrite Adams?" He took great pleasure in pronouncing the word hypocrite: it must have been the longest word he knew. "But as a matter of a fact, I'll tell you. I'm here at the request of, on the behalf of, per pro, and etc., etc., the California Bank, the Western Star and the Grand National Bank whose gold bars you have in that there cave."

I started to see things clearly at last. So that was how the wind was blowing.

"Who gave the banks that fancy idea?" I inquired testily.

"A certain gentl'man what worked for the Adams Express Co. A Mr. 'Mary' O'Callaghan."

The name was like a hammer knocking on my skull.

"You wouldn't believe that double-crosser," says I, trying to coo like a dove, because I remembered how Rourke had pumped lead into "Mary" after his stage-coach hold-up had come unstuck. I guessed he couldn't be feeling much sorrier about "Mary's" death than I was.

"I believe my eyes and nothing else," Rourke answers. "Open up that wall and show me there's no gold in there, and I'll go back to the banks and tell 'em so."

"Like hell do I pull down that wall!" The dove had flown away and the lion was roaring now. "And I'll tell you something, Black Rourke. I don't trust one word from the mouth of a blackguard like you. And I don't trust your pals in the Grand National Bank either: those little angels would sell their mother to get hold of someone else's yellow dust. That's why they sent you here, isn't it? They've stolen all their customers' gold and now they want some more to fill their coffers. I know the crooks!"

There wasn't any more talking after that. Our guns were out and our fingers clenched round the triggers. Rourke's men dashed for cover: there were plenty more boulders strewn round the valley floor. And then the shooting match started. They had more guns, but we had more ammo. We could rest our guns on the wall; they had to aim theirs lying on the ground. We picked out a couple of heads: they knocked out two of my boys. It seemed a stalemate. But the light was fading, and with the dark, Rourke would surely risk coming out of cover. I wasn't wrong in my guess, but there was precious little I could do about it. A soon as night fell—and it comes down like a curtain in those parts—Rourke's men were able to crawl around without our spotting them. We fired off all the time to keep them hopping, but we hadn't a clue where our bullets were going.

Then I see a little fellow jump up not more than three yards in front of the wall. I squash the trigger: he drops down. I can't see whether I have hit him or not.

"Look out. Dynamite!" shouts Jake.

I have just time to catch sight of a fuse sizzling on the floor of the cave. That guy must have lobbed it inside when he stood up. Then bang goes creation! The blast flings me to the ground. The roof starts to rumble. It cracks, breaks up and falls. A deluge of stone comes hurtling down with a noise like ten claps of thunder rolled into one.

When I woke up it seemed as if I couldn't move a joint. That wasn't queer, seeing that there was about half a ton of miscellaneous masonry on my back. I wriggled and squirmed, but it was hopeless. I yelled out to ask if anyone else was alive, and Jake's voice comes out from the back of beyond.

He couldn't come over right away; he was caught up. But by the sound of his groans and the crashes of stones I guessed that he was freeing his way.

"Hold hard, Boss." Jake was standing somewhere close, only I couldn't see because it was pitch as night. "I'll start heaving some of these rocks off of you."

"Just take your time," I shouted back crossly. Another minute of the crushing pain would be too much for me.

We got ourselves out of that mess and began to take stock of our position. We were the only two left alive. Between us and the fresh air outside was at least twenty feet of fallen rock. On the other side was Rourke, no doubt sitting waiting for us as a so-called sportsman wants to shoot a blind pigeon.

There wasn't much alternative but to start hacking away at that wall of rock. If we stayed where we were, we would have starved of hunger and thirst in a few days and died like those nuns they used to wall up in old castles. We had to take a chance on Rourke. With any luck one or more of my coaches would come rolling up to change horses, and they'd either scare Rourke away or else make a dash for it and get news of our imprisonment to the outside world.

As it happened, Rourke had already cleared off before the Salt Lake Express rolled up. He had reckoned that we were all dead inside since he got no answers to his calls, and he had gone off. Fortunately we had picks inside the cavern, and by the time the coach came in we had bashed our way almost through. The coach boys gave us a helping hand to pull us out: we reached the fresh air just twenty-four hours after the cave roof had collapsed.

Guess it's taking me quite a while to get round to that second dent in my flask. It's quite a story when it comes to rolling it out in the proper order.

"Say, Madame, encore un verre de Whisky, if you please."

"Ah! merci, Madame!"

I need a drink here. This is where the riderless coach plunges downhill. Don't take that literal. It's meta—meta—metaphorical or some such word. This is the pay-off. Now listen hard.

That Rourke, the two-timing twister, rides straight off to fetch the Sheriff. If he had thought that he could have got away with it, I'll wager he'd have come back with tools and smashed his own way into the cave. But his money-makers, the bankers, weren't going to let Rourke swipe the kitty. They were quite ready to pay Rourke to do the trigger-work, but when it come to retrieving the dead bird they wanted to be there.

We had just about cleared a decent sized passage into the cave, buried the bodies of our dead boys and had a good wash down, when one of my coaches comes pulling in from the West.

"Sheriff Eaton's headin' this way, Boss," the boys tell me.

"He's got a posse of four score with him, and he's breathing murder at the sound of your name."

I asked who was riding with the Sheriff. They told me that Rourke was up there in the front, and half a score of guys dressed in black like undertakers were bringing up the rear. They were the bankers, I guessed.

"Best be getting out of here, Boss," Jake says, all windy.

"I can do some explaining. Rourke's given the Sheriff a twisted tale. That gold in there belongs to decent people: it's their savings. I'm not handing it over to any man. It ain't mine to give."

"Sheriff Eaton's in no mood to listen to explanations, Boss," the coachman chipped in.

There was truth in that. The Sheriff was a guy who shot first and talked afterwards.

"I'd like to get my knife into that Rourke. I'd twist it round and round in his gizzard." I was furious.

"Wouldn't help, Boss," the coachman said. "Sheriff's not going to stand by and watch you murder his deputy."

"Deputy?" I shouted, dumb-struck.

"Sure thing, Boss. Sheriff's given Black Rourke a deputy's badge for this trip."

"Well, I'll be——" Lucky there weren't ladies present. "Guess the day when the law shakes hands with Black Rourke is the day when I clear out of the West." I spat out the end of my cheroot.

My head seemed to be bursting. It just didn't seem possible. Why, only a year ago the Adams Express Company was a name that was respected even by the worst blackguard on the Barbary Coast. Now blackguard and law officer had joined together to chase me out of business. I suppose if I had sat down and thought it out carefully I would have seen that the best thing for me to do was to stay my ground and argue it out with Sheriff Eaton. But I was hoppin' mad.

"Turn the passengers out of that coach," I commanded. "Jump to it, boys! Jake and Jim, you come with me into the cave and start loading the gold on to the coach."

One of the passengers, a parson, comes up to me to protest.

"Go preach to Sheriff Eaton, mister." I was in no mood to be stopped. "He's more in need of the good Book than I am.

158

I've led a clean life for thirty-five years in this western cesspool, and the only reward I get is to be dubbed a thief and a robber. Scram!"

Guess that parson wasn't the only one who was wondering what was happening. I was running in and out of that cave, shouting orders like a maniac. Water kegs and food had to be loaded aboard. The horses had to be changed. The axles needed greasing—we were going for a long ride.

I asked Jake to come with me, naturally. He and I were linked by that kinship common to survivors of terrible disasters. The other two I chose were lads from the coach crew: I didn't know much about them, but they seemed ready to take a chance.

"Can't get no more gold on board, Boss." Jake was carrying a box full of some old boy's savings. There was no room for it on the coach.

"Guess you'd better leave that box, Jake," I said. "We can't move everything with one coach. Put the box back with the rest of the stuff in the cave and come back here quick."

I found a stick of dynamite in the stores inside. As soon as Jake was out I hurled in that stick just as Rourke's boy had done a day ago. The same thing happened. The mountainside heaved. The roof shook and then came crashing down to block the entrance. Sheriff Eaton would have to lose some of his fat if he wanted to get at what was in the cave. Serve him right. I stood there laughing. I guess I was kind of hysterical by then.

That laugh froze on my face. The Sheriff's posse was riding full tilt up the gulley. It was true: he had fully eighty men with him. But this was no time for counting heads. With a bound I leapt on the coachman's seat: in one hand I seized the reins and in the other the whip.

"Gee up!" I roared, and brought the whip down a smacker. Jake and the boys clambered on to the coach while she was already moving.

"Faster, Boss!" Jake yells from the inside. "Sheriff's coming after us at the gallop." Just as he said that a bullet whistled past on the left, followed by another and another. At this rate our chances were mighty slim. The coach careered up and down as I drove her over the rocky trail at breakneck speed. We were going fast, but the posse was riding faster.

The coach crashed its way down the ravine to the edge of the salt desert. I never turned the brake handle once: it was a miracle that we came to the bottom the right way up and the horses still in harness.

The posse threaded its way down between the rocks like water over a fall. They were on our tails. Jake and the other two boys were firing out of the windows. The posse's bullets were kicking up the ground in front of the coach's path. We couldn't hold out much longer. And then I remembered: the salt marshes!

The marshes lay a hundred yards ahead. I knew them like the back of my hand. Hadn't I charted the first coach route over this desert? Hadn't I spent a week searching for a hard track between the bogs? That week wasn't wasted. At the edge of the wash I swung the coach and plunged into the marshes. It was all right. The wheels continued to turn: we raced on.

Wham! A bullet whizzed home. I felt my thigh tingling. I couldn't spare a hand to explore the damage: both were needed on the reins. I was twisting the horses right and left to keep the coach on to the hard path. If I missed one bend the coach would have plunged headlong into the bog.

Sheriff Eaton's posse spread out across the salt desert in line abreast. Rourke knew about the danger of the marshes, but the others were strangers. They rode their horses straight into the bog, suspecting nothing: within two minutes their horses were floundering in a morass of mushy salt.

As the coach twisted around I caught sight of the posse. And what a sight it was! Fully three-quarters of them were squirming in the bog, yelling, shrieking, begging. I fancy that if I'd have gone back to pull out Sheriff Eaton he would have thrown his arms around me and pinned a deputy's badge on me there and then. But I wasn't feeling like making any experiments.

When the coach was through the bog I slowed her down. That thigh of mine was still throbbing. But there wasn't any blood. Strange thing! I couldn't make it out. Guess it called for a swig. And then, when I tried to pull out my flask, the whole thing was clear. A slug had got itself lodged right in the metal of the flask. That certainly was a close shave! That Scotsman had said that maybe the flask would save my life one day. He must have been a prophet besides being quite a hand at forging steel.

Four days and four nights I hustled on. There was no one

*"How can any authority stop the cattle-rustlers from tearing
down our fences night after night?"*

following the coach, I don't suppose, but the fear spurred me on. The two men I had taken with Jake and me started to become troublesome. They wanted some shut-eye. The lack of sleep made me irritable. I drew my gun on them.

"Keep the coach moving," I said, "or you'll stay behind by yourselves with a hole in your skull."

They didn't answer, but they looked daggers.

When at last we fetched up at a township over the other side of the Rockies we were all dead beat. For two dimes I'd have pulled up at the saloon and fixed up a doss-down for all of us. But it wouldn't have been safe leaving that coachload unguarded in the street. Why, its payload was worth well over a million dollars! So I parked the stage-coach out in the prairie a half-mile out of the burg.

Jake said he would stay by the coach while we went into town. I promised that I'd come back in a couple of hours after having a wash-down and a bit of grub. As for the other two, I reckoned that it was safer for them to stay away for the night. The prospect of having those two galuts around after an evening's boozing wasn't appealing. They might get some ideas into their heads when their bellies were full of liquor.

The three of us got into the saloon together. The barkeep and I were old pals. We'd known each other in Kansas City. He and I got yarning. After a couple of hours and quite a few tumblers of Scotch I reckoned it was about time I headed back to give Jake a turn in town.

I'm not more than thirty yards from the coach when a shot rings out. It was pitch dark at the time, so it wasn't possible to see what was happening.

"Jake!" I yell. "Are you all right?"

Jake doesn't answer but a couple of Colts spit out at me.

I'm not too steady on my feet. Liquor on an empty tummy makes a man feel that he's floating along like an angel. I fumble for my gun, but it won't come out of the holster. Not knowing quite what I'm doing, I start running towards the coach.

"Get out of here," a voice calls out.

So that was it—the thought comes to me in a flash—those two rats have sneaked back here to hi-jack the coach. I rushed at the man who had spoken. I felt a sharp pain in my face, but I was too mad to stop. My hands caught him round the neck.

It was like wringing a chicken. There was a little gurgle and that was the end of him.

I stooped down and picked up his rod. The other man wasn't to be seen. But he'd seen me. I felt his elbow clinch round my neck, and then I was swung right over his shoulder. He emptied his Colt at what he thought was me lying on the ground. Three quick shots he fired. How he missed I don't know, but most likely he was too excited to know what he was doing.

Now was my chance before he reloaded. I had dropped my gun while being thrown. But I still had my knife. The fall had sobered me up quicker than any bucket of cold water. I whipped out my knife and slung it. The blade went straight through his chest, and he sunk to the ground with a groan.

Jake was past saving. When I found him in the dark he was muttering away. I put my head to his mouth, but I couldn't catch a word of what he was saying. He was lying propped up against the side of the coach with the blood gushing out of his shoulder. I ripped off my coat and tore out the lining to make a tourniquet. I started to put the bandage on him, but as soon as I touched him there was an uncontrollable shaking of his body. He went out like a candle flame that flickers before it dies.

Poor old Jake! I was just thinking what a good pal he'd been when I heard the sound of voices. The gunshots had brought all the boys out of the saloon.

The situation was none too healthy. It would take some explaining how three men came to be lying on the ground dead and the coachload of gold—it was asking too much of human nature to expect the boys to leave that alone.

I had the four horses in harness quicker than horses have ever been harnessed before or since. The crowd came running on to the scene as I was climbing up on to the driver's seat. There was a tremendous hullabaloo when they saw that I was making a getaway. They had heard gunshots, and they didn't like the idea of a man doing a bunk without answering any questions.

"Grab him!" they shouted. "Haul him down!"

"String him up!" someone called.

I didn't wait to listen to any more suggestions. I cracked the whip and drove straight through them. When they realized what was going on they let off their guns fast and furious. But it was inky dark and the horses were pulling mighty fast.

It was a pity leaving Jake there without a cross over his head, but I guess he would have understood my reasons.

In those days one couldn't get a coach very far without a crew of men. The tracks were swimming with mud. Every few miles the wheels would stick fast, and the only way of getting on was to have the men jump off to push. Somewhere round the early hours of that morning in a downpour of rain my coach got bogged down. I coaxed the horses, I hauled at their guide ropes, I whipped them, but it was no good. That coach was heavy, and that coach was stuck good and proper.

What was to be done? I guess I was too exhausted to think it out. I was dead beat: hadn't had a sleep for over three days. I just sunk on the ground like a weary child and went off into a sleep as deep as the Pacific Ocean.

When I woke up it was pitch dark. I'd slept through the whole day, and here it was some time in the middle of the next night. Cold, wet and hungry, I got to my feet and paced up and down to keep warm. There was not much choice. Most of the gold would have to be abandoned. The largest ingots and the odd jewels that were on board could be stowed in sacks and tied on the horses.

I went to work with a driving will. Three-quarters of the coachload I carried to a place off the beaten track and buried in a hole, marking the spot with a code sign. Then I set fire to the coach: no need to leave any traces. How delicious that fire was. It warmed me right through. The light was just coming up over the plains when the job was finished. Each of the three horses was loaded with a couple of home-made saddle-bags: the fourth carried me.

It was a nightmare of a journey. A man travelling alone with four horses attracts attention and picks up unwelcome companions. A couple of Mexicans joined up with me. I did my best to discourage them.

"I'd be getting along if I were you. This horse of mine needs shoeing. She can only hobble along."

"That all right, señor," the older Mexican replied. "We got all time in the world."

We rode along silently for a while. I tried a new scheme.

"Say, boys," I said politely. "I must have forgotten my billy-can where I made camp last night. I guess I'll go back to fetch it."

"I go fetch for you, señor." One of the Mexicans had already wheeled round his horse. The scheme collapsed.

Gold has a smell that is more powerful than any perfume used by woman; there isn't a man alive who can tear himself away from a sack of gold. It wasn't any use pretending to those Mexicans that there was anything else in the saddle-bags; they were too heavy. I tried to get them to understand that the gold didn't belong to me, but it would have been easier to teach an oyster how to walk.

"Oho, señor!" José, the older Mex, nodded his unshaven head. "Gold not yours. You have gold all by yourself. You very clever robber. We stay with you." He gave me a broad wink.

It wasn't any good. They were as wide awake as I was.

I had hoped to give them the slip at night. I got up, tiptoed over to where they were lying. They seemed fast asleep. They didn't move while I lugged the bags up on to the saddle and strapped them. But when I jumped on my own horse they bounded up, and before my animal had gone twenty paces, there they were on horseback, one on either side of me.

"Señor not sleep." José spoke in a mocking tone. "We not sleep either. Señor like ride by moon. We like ride by moon too."

There was no shaking them off: they were like flies round a cow's eyes in the summer-time. They were about as trustworthy as a couple of maggots. There's a saying out West: If you can't trust a man, buy him. So I bought these two Mexics, hiring them as my servants at the princely pay of an ounce of gold dust every Monday.

If I thought that my troubles would end there, I was in for a rude shock; but I had no such thought. Those cursed Mexics spread the word down the trail that I was riding with a sultan's ransom of gold in my saddle-bags. Flies sticking to fly-paper were not in it. By the time I got somewhere near St. Louis I had thirty or so men riding behind me like a general's escort of cavalry.

"Señor," José would come up to me. "Señor need very good man polish his boots. I got very good man. Only thirty dollars a week."

It didn't take me long to spot that game. The very good boot polisher would get ten dollars, José would pocket twenty. But I couldn't say no, at least not until I got to St. Louis and could turn over the gold to a place of safety.

"Oh, very well, José!" I replied with a sigh. "Guess you had better hire him."

St. Louis has seen some mighty queer customers before and since, but I doubt if an odder gang ever came riding in than Harry Adams with six sacks of gold and jewels, two Mexican stewards and a couple of dozen hoboes, out-of-work cow-punchers, down-at-heel prospectors, on-the-run wide boys signed up as grooms, waiters, valets, flunkeys and the like.

I rode up to the main hotel. "Have them bring my baggage up to my room," I called to José.

"Lift sacks!" José kicked the backside of one of his under-lings. "Hey, you fellow. Help that bum carry sacks." And he gave another lad a punch in the back.

The hotel manager was bowing his sweating head to the ground. He couldn't have got no lower if I'd been the King of England.

Up in my room I didn't waste any time. I set the younger Mexic to guard the door. José insisted on keeping me company.

"You get lonely by yourself, señor." He winked like I wanted to clout him, but his pal would have come in, and his pal could throw a knife better than any man I had seen.

"You know how to sew, José?" I asked him.

"Si, señor, my daddy was tailor man."

"Great! Then get cracking with this needle! I want you to make me a special kind of waistcoat." And I explained to him that I wanted a waistcoat that would have sewn into its lining a couple of hundred strips of gold.

I'll give old José this much: he sewed like a magician. He had finished the job in a couple of hours.

"Now, José make for himself same kind of waistcoat," he said as he handed me over my new garment.

"Oh! I don't think you need bother about that, José. One's enough."

"No, no, señor. I think me and my amigo get cold without such coats."

I stared into his eyes. The oily little maggot! All the same, I couldn't help admiring his persistency.

"Very well then," I said with a shrug of the shoulders. "But only two more. I don't want that whole army of yours dressed in golden waistcoats."

The waistcoat fitted excellently, though it weighed me down almost to my knees until I got used to it. Now there were those sacks of gold to be looked after. A town the size of St. Louis ought to have a bank that was better than the hole-in-a-wall affairs we had out West.

Are you wondering why I wasn't going to turn in the gold in that waistcoat? Well, I'll tell you. I reckoned on getting my own back on that crook gang of bankers, and on Messrs. Wells, Fargo too. My aim was to get to Washington, D.C., and start pulling a few strings. It was time that the Government sent out a commission to California to put things straight. Pulling strings in Washington was an expensive business in those days. That's why I needed that gold, see!

There was a shindy going on outside the hotel room. I stuck my head out to see what was going on.

"Adams!" a voice called. "I arrest you in the name of the people of the United States."

"What for?" I called out, holding the door half open.

"Murder! Murder of your three companions and robbing a stage-coach."

"It's a damned lie, Sheriff."

"Will you surrender or have I got to come and get you?"

I slammed the door just as a bullet whizzed to the place where I had been standing.

"Hey, José." I started running to the window. "You'd better get out of here if you aim to live."

But he didn't have a chance to make up his mind one way or the other. The door was thrown open: a volley of bullets from half a dozen guns cracked into the room. I just caught sight of José tumbling off the bed on which he had been sitting before I crashed through the window and jumped.

Lucky I fell on my feet: it was a drop of over twenty feet. No time to dust my pants: the bullets were whistling around me. I picked up my heels and ran round the corner into the main street. There was a crowd of folk roaming up and down the roadway, taking the air before the dark finally settled down. The sheriff's men came running round after me, but I got myself tucked away in the crowd.

"*Hey, José.*" *I started running to the window.*
"*You'd better get out of here . . . .*"

"Murderer!" shouted the Marshals. The folks started turning towards each other to ask what was happening.

"There he is!" I said, excitedly taking hold of a passer-by's arm. "Look, he's just turning round the corner."

"After him!" roared the passer-by, throwing away his cigar and starting to run.

Within a few moments the whole crowd of citizens started in hot pursuit. I was right in the thick of them, enjoying myself immensely. As soon as there was half a chance I dodged into a doorway to let the milling crowd go by.

It was then that I strode into a little tailor's shop and changed suits. There were a couple of guys eyeing me as I walked down the street. I reckoned that a change of outfit might throw them off scent. And sure it did. They were standing outside the shop door as I came out. They looked me up and down.

"Evening!" I said amiably.

"Evening," they replied reluctantly: I was evidently not the fellow they were looking for.

"Waiting for someone?" I cracked, just to rub it in.

"Sure thing," they answered, baring their teeth, feeling for the butt of their guns. I strolled off, whistling a tune. Once out of their sight I legged it fast for the railroad terminus. In a couple of hours' time I was huddled up in a corner seat of the New York express.

I was certainly in a fix. I didn't know quite what to do next, so I opened the newspaper to try to take my mind off things. There it was on the front page:

CALIFORNIA GOVERNOR CALLS ON NATION
HUE AND CRY FOR ADAMS

My eyes leaped along the lines; my heart raced quicker than the engine. It seemed as if the Governor had promised a group of California bankers that he would not rest until Harry Adams had been brought to justice. The bankers were offering 10,000 dollars reward for my capture, dead or alive. I was charged with systematic robbery of stage-coach packages, robbery of over a thousand gold bars which I was said to have replaced with gold-plated lead blocks. Added to this were charges of murdering seven of Rourke's men and wilfully resisting arrest. A footnote to the column added that the Sheriff of Red Rock wanted Harry Adams in connection with the murder of his three companions in crime—Jake and the other two coach boys.

There was no hope of getting anyone to listen to me in Washington. My best chance was to lie low in New York. They said it was a big city where a man could easily get lost.

I found lodgings in the old part of the town. But it wasn't long before I came up against trouble. At the end of the first week the landlady came for the rent. I handed her a strip of gold. Putting on a smirk of a smile I quipped: "That ought to keep you happy for a good few weeks, lady."

"What's the good of that to me, mister?" She looked even more sour than usual. "This ain't California. You pay me in dollar coins or you get out."

There was only one solution—the way I had hoped to avoid —to go round to a bank and turn in the gold for money in exchange.

"Just a minute, sir." The bank teller eyed me queerly. "I'll weigh the strip."

He came back after a while. "The manager says will you please step into his office for a few words."

My head was a whirl. Should I go or make a dash for it? No! best brazen it out. I followed the teller into the inner office. The manager stood up to greet me: there were a couple of men, one on each side of him.

"Ah! Mr. Johnson," he says, for Johnson was the name I had given. "You don't happen to have met a man called Adams in your travels?"

"Adams," I said, rolling the word round my tongue. "Adams? No, I guess not."

"A dangerous murderer," chimed in one of the henchmen.

"Curious," mumbled the manager. He was eyeing some piece of paper on his desk. "You wouldn't happen to be Mr. Adams yourself, would you?"

"Stick 'em up!" I levelled my gun at them. I had caught them unawares. "Now turn to the wall, gentlemen." They hesitated, but obeyed. I seized the chance and backed out of the door, keeping them covered as I went.

"Good morning," I called to the teller, and shot out of that bank as if my tail was on fire.

That night, when the mist had come up from the water, I

crept down to the harbour. After a walk around, I came upon
a Dutchman with her sails all furled and her gang-plank just
being lowered. The captain didn't ask questions. He was half
sozzled, so probably he couldn't. But he wasn't too far gone to
recognize the gleam of half a dozen gold strips.

"First-class passenger." He was beaming all over as he
stuffed the gold into his desk drawer. "Damn good man,
Yankee." And he landed me a whack on the back that nearly
laid me flat, but it was only a drunk's way of saying "Howdy".

Yeah! That's the way I came to Europe. They say that all
good Americans come to Paris to die. Guess that's why I came
here.

"Encore un whisky, Madame."

This stuff keeps me going—as long as I can afford to buy it.

"Oui, a double one, Madame."

I spend five gold strips a year keeping alive. And I've got just
five strips left. Oh! They're after me all right. But they won't
find me. I'll win the last round. I'll be dead before they come.

"Have a drink, stranger! That's right. Now drink a toast,
damn you! Drink to the ghost of Harry Adams! Drink it up,
man. Ain't my story worth a drink?"

Yes, sir! The ghost will have the last laugh yet.

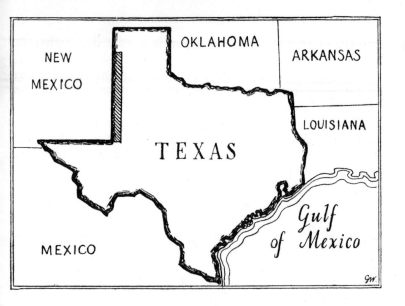

THE HELL-HOLE OF THE WEST

It had been known as the hell-hole of the West for many years: a description which, thought Sheriff Ira Aten grimly to himself, seemed to be a pretty apt one.

Bert Johnson, the manager of the XIT ranch, had just finished speaking; and the tale that he had told had given Ira much food for thought. He drew slowly on his pipe as his eyes travelled over the five men seated round the table in the small front room of the manager's house.

The manager's house was also the headquarters of the XIT ranch; and the five men present were the manager himself, Buck Miller (the ranch's head cowboy), Ira's own two assistants, young Ed Connel and old Joe Saunders, and Jim Gallagher, the Mayor of the town of Peterville—which, though some twenty miles away from the headquarters of the ranch, was still the nearest town of any size to the ranch's great sprawling territory.

The five pairs of eyes were intently fixed on Ira. Old Joe's looked slightly baffled; young Ed's were full of suppressed excitement. Bert's were anxious; Buck's alert and watchful; and (behind the thick glasses that covered them) the Mayor's eyes were steadily and firmly looking at Ira, although no sign of

171

expression showed itself on his rather pale and rather fat face.

Ira kept on drawing at his pipe; and there was a dead silence in the small room. The silence lasted so long that old Joe became suddenly impatient.

"For God's sake, Ira," he exploded, "are you going to smoke yourself to death, or are you going to take on this job or not? We all want to know; but sitting here like a bunch of stuffed monkeys does none of us any good."

The Mayor laughed.

"Don't rush him, Joe," he said. "Ira knows his own mind."

"Maybe he does," said Joe, "but I want to know what's in that mind of his—and I want to know it right here and right now. We are either staying or going. But I want to know which."

"So do I," said Bert. "Ira, you *must* help us. This ranch is a hundred miles long and twenty miles wide. Buck and I do our best to control it. But the job has just become too much for us."

The Mayor gently intervened.

"I help too, Bert," he said.

"Of course you do," answered Bert warmly. "I wasn't forgetting you, Jim, but you are twenty miles away and——"

The Mayor completed the sentence.

"And have no right *in law* to exercise any kind of jurisdiction over the ranch. I only wish," he added regretfully, "that I had."

Buck spoke for the first time, and his voice was both cold and angry.

"What blasted difference would it make," he asked, "if you *had* that authority? How can any authority (even a mayor's authority) stop the cattle-rustlers from tearing down our fences night after night? Authority counts for nothing, but what does count is men and bullets. Don't you agree, Sheriff?"

Joe's eyes looked at Buck's handsome but strained face, and he answered instead of Ira.

"Do you know," he said approvingly, "Buck is talking plain common horse sense, Ira, if you don't mind my saying so."

Ira's eyes flickered, but he still said nothing.

"Oh, come on, Ira," said Bert. "What is the answer? Yes or no?"

172

"There's too damned much talk here," suddenly shouted Buck, "and too little action. I'm going."

He rose to leave.

"Sit down," said Ira. He knocked the ashes out of his pipe. "I have made my decision. I shall take this job on."

The relief in the room was obvious and immense.

"Thank you, Sheriff," said Bert quietly. "I will sleep easier tonight."

"I told you, Joe," laughed the Mayor, "not to rush Ira."

Joe was a little abashed.

"I've known him—man and boy—for nigh on fifty years. But he's always so cussed slow at making up his mind that he sometimes gives me the creeps. Sitting there smoking and thinking when we ought to be out riding and doing our best to catch these galoots and pump 'em as full of lead as they can hold."

"Hear, hear," shouted Buck. "That's the sort of talk I like to listen to." His face (in spite of its strain) was shining with excitement. "If we catch them tonight, the four of us can do something that these blasted hoodlums just won't ever forget. Come on, let's go."

"Coming, son," said Joe.

He and Ed stood up. Ira started to fill his pipe again but did not move from his chair.

"Come on, Ira," shouted Joe.

Ira finished filling his pipe and yawned slightly.

"Is there any need, Buck," he asked, "for us to come tonight? It's almost midnight already."

"What do you mean?" stammered Buck. "Of course there is."

"Why?" grunted Ira. "*We* are all tired after three hard days' riding to get here. Is there any *real* need for *us* to go out *tonight*?"

Buck looked at him uncomprehendingly.

"I just don't get you," he said.

Ira's answering voice had a tinge of impatience in it.

"We are all tired——"

"I ain't," interjected Joe indignantly.

"Nor I," said Ed, half-blushing as he spoke. (Ed, by the way, was only eighteen years old and very shy into the bargain, and hardly ever spoke when he was in the company of older men.)

173

Ira disregarded the interruptions and went flatly on.

"We *are* all tired, though, if need be, we could ride tonight. And, Buck, if you *know* or *suspect* that there's going to be a raid we *will* come. Otherwise, we stay here."

"What?" gasped Joe.

"Otherwise," repeated Ira, "we stay here."

The expression on Buck's face was indescribable.

"So the fine Sheriff and his fine friends aren't coming?" he sneered.

"Not," said Ira carefully, "unless anything is likely to happen. But Buck hasn't told me yet whether anything *is* likely to happen or not." He looked steadily at Buck.

It was Buck's turn to explode.

"How the hell should I know," he shouted angrily at Ira, "whether anything *is* likely to happen tonight? I'm just a cowboy. The rustlers don't tell *me* beforehand where or when they are going to strike. But most nights," he said (very significantly), "they do strike somewhere or other; and if only people would *help* me to stop them, instead of talk, talk, talk about *how* to stop them——" His voice rose to an almost hysterical scream.

"Buck," said Bert, "sit down."

Buck glared at Bert.

"Why should I sit down?" He was going to say more, but the Mayor's cool voice added: "Buck, please sit down."

The Mayor turned to Ira.

"The strain of all this, Sheriff, is tearing Buck's nerves to pieces. He's the finest head cowboy this ranch has ever had."

"That's true," said Bert.

"But night after night these raids do occur, and always at the most unexpected places. If we knew anything beforehand we could——" The Mayor took his glasses off and polished them. "We could rush all the men of the ranch—and, even though I have no legal authority over the ranch itself"—he smiled—"the two or three men under my control—to the danger spot." His steel-blue eyes were steadily regarding Ira.

Ira said: "Yes, I see, Mayor," and drew on his pipe. The Mayor put his glasses back on.

"That's the position, Sheriff," Bert said. "With a ranch like

this we will never know where the attack will come from next."
Buck got up.

"Talk, talk. Nothing but damned talk. Go on, talk your
blasted silly heads off, all of you. I'm going." He strode out of
the room.

"Ira," shouted Joe, "what in hell are you playing at? Why
don't we go with him? If there *is* a raid tonight he'll be killed
and it will be only your own fault—you obstinate old cuss!"

Ed said pleadingly: "Could I go with him, sir?"

Ira pulled out his pack of patience cards and answered: "No."
But his voice was so firm and decisive, as it gave that answer,
that Joe sank back into his chair. Joe knew Ira of old, and he
also knew an order when he heard one.

Grumbling and muttering, he said: "Okay: what now?"

"I'm going to play patience," said Ira, "for a few minutes,
and you two chaps are going to bed."

Obediently, Joe and Ed left the room.

Joe was still grumbling and muttering when he reached his
and Ed's bedroom.

"I don't know, Ed," he said as he started to undress for bed,
"what that old cuss is playing at. *We* ought to have been out
now with Buck."

"I think so," said Ed, "but he always knows best; and I'm
not going to undress. You never know. Something may happen
after all."

Joe looked at Ed.

"Okay, son," he said thoughtfully as he slowly started putting
his clothes back on again.

The two sat down together. Both were thinking. Neither
spoke.

Down below they heard the sound of the front door open and
Ira saying to the Mayor: "Well, good night, Mayor. I'll get
really started on this job tomorrow."

They heard the Mayor's laughing reply.

"Whenever it suits you, Sheriff, but I expect we'll have to
wait till you find all the blacks to go on all the reds of that
patience game of yours."

They heard Ira say: "Patience, Mayor, is a very highly rated
virtue amongst the people who have it."

"It's a virtue I have myself."

"Good night," said Ira.

"Good night, too," added Bert's voice.

The door closed again.

Bert and Ira must have gone back together to the small sitting-room, because for some ten minutes or so no more noise came from downstairs. But then heavy lumbering feet began to climb the stairs.

Their door opened and in the doorway stood Bert. He glanced round the small room.

"You boys comfortable?" he asked.

"Very," said Ed.

"You haven't got your clothes off yet," said Bert somewhat accusingly.

"Yarning together," retorted Joe. "Ed's a great one for talking when we're alone."

Ed blushed and Bert perched on the bed.

"Joe," he said (and his eyes were heavy and anxious as he said it), "what's wrong with that there Sheriff of yours?"

Joe blinked.

"Nothing that I know of," he answered. "What do you mean?"

"Well, he's acting very queerly. I thought he'd have been out and after these raiders like a shot. He wasted no time—way back in fifty-six—when he caught the Colorado gang, or in sixty-two when he rounded up the Wyoming boys."

"I know," said Joe. "I was there with him—both times, and you never saw anything faster than old Ira."

"Well, what's he up to now," said the manager irritably, "sitting about doing nothing except playing that damn silly patience game? Where will that get us? He was asked by the owners to come here because they thought that a man like him could clear up this mess. But all he's done so far is to rile Buck, and I don't think the Mayor is too pleased with him either."

Joe's loyalty leapt to the surface.

"What the hell has it got to do with this whether the Mayor is pleased or not? Who's this Mayor, anyway?" His face was red with rage. "Ira was sent for, wasn't he? Ira was asked to do the job and has said he will, hasn't he? If you aren't satisfied, just go downstairs and tell Ira. Tell him yourself. Go on, go

176

and tell him, and tell that fat-bellied Mayor of yours too to keep his nose out of other people's business."

"Now, now," said Ed soothingly.

"Shut up, Ed," growled Joe. "This is serious, and anyone that insults Ira insults me too."

"I didn't insult Ira," said Bert as he edged quickly out of the room.

As the door closed behind him, Joe glared after him.

"Of all the cheek! Insulting old Ira like that!"

"I don't think he really meant it," answered Ed. "Ira *is* acting a bit oddly."

"I *know*," confessed Joe, "but he just riled me with these cracks about Ira."

They sat together in silence for a moment.

"You see, Ed," said Joe, "I just don't understand this myself, and I feel worried. What's going to happen next?"

Ed said: "Wait and see."

They had not long to wait. There was a light tap on the door, followed by a swift whispered conversation between Joe, Ed and the person who had tapped on the door.

CHAPTER II

It was seven o'clock on the morning of the following day when Buck came back and burst into the little office.

Ira was sprawling in his chair in front of the fire, obviously asleep. The patience cards were lying before him.

Buck stood over him and sneered.

"Wake up, you damned fool," he shouted. "What sort of sheriff are you?"

Ira woke up with a start. His eyes blinked as he looked at Buck towering over him.

"Good God!" he said, jumping to his feet. "What's happened?"

"Can't you see?" yelled Buck back in answer.

Ira *could* see.

Buck's clothes were covered with blood, and blood was still slowly oozing from a wound in his right forearm.

"Let's see that wound," said Ira sharply. "It may be serious."

177

Buck rolled up his sleeve, but his hands trembled so much as he did so that Ira had to help him.

The noise had awakened Bert: and Bert suddenly clumped into the room.

"What's going on here?" he said.

"Buck's been wounded. Look." Ira showed him the knife-cut on Buck's arm. "A nasty cut, Buck," he added, "but not serious. A half-inch farther over and it *would* have been serious. It would have got an artery, but it didn't; and, apart from having a sore arm for a day or two, you will be all right."

Buck relaxed.

"Good," he said. "I'd like to sit down." He sat down. He was looking very pale and strained. Ira's eyes were watching him intently.

"You need sleep and rest, my lad," he said, "and you are going off to bed in two minutes. But can you just tell us quickly what happened?"

"Yes," said Bert. "What did happen?"

"Well, I thought I would start my inspection at Station Six."

"Station Six?" echoed Ira.

The manager explained, as Ira looked at the plans of the ranch.

"There are forty-five stations in the ranch, and they all have numbers; and at each station we have, day and night, not less than three men on constant duty. There is also a reserve force of twenty men whom we move about from station to station on a general patrol."

"And they've never yet—this precious reserve force of yours —been at the right station at the right time," yelled Buck. "They're always somewhere else. Break-in at Ten, reserve force at Sixteen. Break-in at Sixteen, reserve force at Ten."

"That's not my fault, Buck," said Bert gently, "and you know it. The owners just won't give me enough men to cover the whole of this ranch properly. I've got to use my reserve force to the best of my own judgment, and you yourself are always consulted as to where they should go. That's right, isn't it, Buck?"

Buck hesitated.

"Is that right?" asked Ira sternly.

Buck looked at the manager and at Ira.

"That," he said slowly, "is right."

He tossed his head angrily, and added bitterly: "I've been trying to run this ranch for two years with about a couple of hundred half-caste Indians, Chinks and God knows what else to help me. He"—gesturing contemptuously at the manager—"has always promised more help, but none has come except a Sheriff who plays cards and two friends of his who seem to be frightened to go out at nights."

"Wrong there," said Joe.

Ed and he had just come into the room.

"We have been out, Buck," Joe said as he started to undo his spurs.

"Where?" said Bert.

"Just generally riding round. Ed and I like to know the general set-up of any place on which we are going to do a job."

"But where exactly have you been?" repeated Bert.

"Stations One, Two, Three and Four," answered Joe promptly Tomorrow it will be Stations Five, Six, and so on."

There was a curious smile on Buck's face as he said: "So you didn't get to Station Six tonight?"

"Not tonight," answered Joe comfortably; "Station Six is tomorrow. Good gosh, Buck," he said suddenly, "what in tarnation has happened to you?"

"Buck's been wounded," said Ira shortly, "and I want to hear his story. So just shut up, Joe, for a few minutes. What happened, Buck?"

"There isn't really a lot to tell," Buck said as he puffed eagerly at the cigarette Ed had thoughtfully handed to him. "I went to Station Six as I have said. Everything was quiet there, and I thought that I would ride over to Station Eleven. That's the nearest one due east from Six," he explained.

"Yes," said Ira, "go on."

"Well," drawled Buck, "all was quiet at Eleven too. So I just started to ride back to Six. But before I ever got near it, I heard the roar of stampeding cattle coming towards me. They were our cattle, but there was nothing I could do to stop them, so I let them go and waited for the men who were driving them."

"Good," said Ira. "That was the best policy. Did you see the men?"

"Well, yes and no," replied Buck.

"Did you shoot them up?" queried Ed eagerly.

179

"Joe," said Buck, casting a rather pitying look at Ed, "would you if you were one against twenty, start shooting the twenty up?"

Joe whistled. "Twenty! Good gosh, I'd have run for my life. I'm as good a shot as anybody in the whole of this here State——"

"Don't brag," interrupted Ira with a grin.

Joe grinned back, but continued: "I can cope with three, five or maybe even seven, but twenty's too darned much for any one man, even me or even perhaps Ed." He grinned at Ed and looked approvingly at Buck. "What did you do, son?"

Buck suppressed a great yawn. "Got down into the ditch and watched them."

"Good for you," said Joe. "Did you recognize any of them?"

"Not quite," answered Buck, but there was such a queer halting tone in his voice as he answered that both Bert and Ira looked sharply at him.

Bert said: "Come on, Buck. Tell us more."

"Buck's very sleepy," said Ira gently. "I think he should go to bed."

"Not yet," said Bert. "I want to know more of this. What did that yes and no answer mean?"

"Well, they were all masked: so I didn't see their faces, but as they passed the ditch the horse of one stumbled. The rider fell heavily to the ground but picked himself up quickly and began to remount his horse. I dived for him but he slung a knife at me. It hit me in the arm——"

"A knife!" said Ira wonderingly. "Didn't he shoot?"

"No," said Buck, "he *did* not." There was some significance in his voice that neither Ira nor his two friends understood: but Buck was looking steadily at the manager who was looking equally steadily back.

"Go on," said the manager, stroking his chin.

"I tried to grapple with him, but he managed to get on to his horse."

"Didn't you follow him?" asked Ira.

"No. I *did* not."

"But why in hell not?" exploded Joe. The bewilderment on Joe's face was intense and was reflected on both Ed's and Ira's. Buck said slowly: "Well, you see, I saw his gold tooth for a moment as his mask half-lifted from his face when I grappled with him."

"Saw his gold tooth," yelped Joe. "Are you off your head, Buck? Gold teeth never stopped me from chasing a rustler."

"Quiet, Joe," said the manager. "I think Buck is trying to tell me something."

"Then what in tarnation is it?" growled Joe.

"Buck, you can speak freely. We're all friends here."

Buck looked round. His face was taut and tense as he said: "There are lots of men round here with gold teeth, but if you see a small fat man with *one* gold tooth in his head and then get a knife thrown at you instead of a bullet—well, I ask you."

"Well, ask me," said Joe bitterly. "Ask me. Go on, keep on asking me, because I don't know the blasted answer. Maybe Bert does." He looked at Bert. So did Ira. Bert hesitated.

"Come on, Bert," said Ira.

"Well," said Bert slowly, "I know nothing, but there is a very big guess in my mind, and such an extraordinary guess that I hesitate even to put it into words."

"A guess," said Ira, "is only a guess, but guesses can sometimes be very useful."

Bert ruminated.

"No," he said, "it can't be him."

"Who?"

Bert was still ruminating and didn't answer for a minute, but then his face suddenly cleared and he began to laugh softly to himself.

"What the hell are you laughing at?" barked Buck angrily.

"Sorry, Buck. But I think you were wrong. I've just remembered something."

"Oh, for God's sake, get on," shouted Joe, jumping to his feet. "I'm getting tired of all this damned talk and palaver, and that's all we've done since we came here. First, Ira; now you. Both of you making mysteries out of what is nothing but plain robberies and killings. That poor——"

"Will you please shut up, Joe?" shouted Ira so suddenly and angrily that Joe blenched. He looked furiously for a moment at Ira but, under Ira's stern gaze, sat down, muttering something to himself.

"Now, go on, Bert," said Ira, "and no more interruptions from you, Joe, *if you please*. This is serious."

"Serious, my foot," snarled Joe. "There's nothing serious round here." Very ostentatiously he pulled out of his pocket a pack of the dirtiest playing-cards that anyone had ever seen and elaborately spread them out before him.

"I like a game of patience now and then myself," he said, still glaring furiously at Ira.

Ira's lips twitched.

"Go on, Bert."

Bert said, very soberly and quietly:

"There are two men, Sheriff, near this ranch who are both small and fat and have one gold tooth each in their head. One of them was once a professional knife-thrower, and the other cannot easily fire a gun with his right hand because he lost the whole of his right index-finger in a shooting match ten years ago. He can, however"—he paused—"throw a knife."

"Now I begin to see," said Ira softly.

The manager's quiet voice went on. "One is——"

"The one you first thought of," said Ira. "I saw the Mayor's gold tooth and his missing finger as we were talking to him."

Bert looked sharply at him. "Good for you, Ira."

"Buck, you thought it was the Mayor, didn't you?" asked Ira.

"Well," said Buck rather defensively, "I wasn't really sure, but if it is the Mayor that's really behind all this, I thought it better not to pursue him, but to come back here instead and tell you, so that you people could sort out what to do next."

"Quite right," said Ira.

Joe was no longer even pretending to look at his cards. He got up and patted Buck on the back. "That makes sense to me, son." He turned to Ira (his bad humour was all gone and his face wore a delighted smile). "We ain't never yet caught any mayors, Ira. This is going to be fun."

Buck yawned again.

"Off to bed, Buck," said Ira. "You've told us all we want to know, and you need sleep; and that wound needs dressing too. Take him up, Ed, and dress it for him, and don't start talking. He needs sleep."

Ed blushed. He admired Buck: and the idea of talking to Buck had already entered his head.

"I'll go too," said Joe.

"You'll stay here," said Ira sharply. "We haven't finished yet."

Buck and Ed went off.

"Haven't finished yet," gasped Joe. "It's an open-and-shut case. It's that Mayor. Don't like him, anyway. Sitting there with those thick glasses on most of the time, and hardly ever letting you see his eyes. I like to see their eyes."

"So do I," said Ira. "But what of this other one, Bert, that you mentioned?"

"Don't misunderstand me," said Bert. "Buck's news was a shock to me, and I instinctively jumped to the same conclusion as he seems to have done. But, on reflection, I think we were both wrong. That was *not* the Mayor. The Mayor is a very honourable and upright man and has been doing his best; in spite of his thick glasses"—he smiled at Joe—"to preserve law and order here. He has been a great help to me."

Joe was dumbfounded.

"Well, if it wasn't him, who was it?"

Ed came back into the room.

"Fixed him up?" asked Ira.

"Yes," said Ed, "and cleaned up the blood on his clothes too."

Ira threw a very quick glance at Ed. There was something odd in the glance and Ed blushed.

"Did you start talking to him?"

Ed blushed even deeper.

"Just a few minutes," he stammered. "He wants me to ride with him to Station Twelve this afternoon.

Ira looked affectionately at Ed. "And you want to go?" he said.

"Yes."

"Then go."

"Thank you."

"What about me?" barked Joe.

"Joe," said Ira firmly, "*you* talk far too much and don't listen enough. I'm still waiting to hear from Bert who the other man might have been. Now then, Bert."

"The other one," answered Bert, "is Delrio."

"And who in hell is Delrio?" shouted Joe.

"The owner of the only saloon in Peterville—the worst spot in the whole of the town. Murderers, pickpockets—all the scum of the earth—and even some of our own cowboys go there. The Mayor has done his best to clean it up, but Delrio and that Chink manager of his seem to get away with it all the time."

"Why?" said Ira.

"I just don't know," answered Bert. "But the Mayor seems to think that Delrio has some kind of powerful protection behind the scenes."

"That's the Mayor himself," stormed Joe. "I'm telling you, Ira, it's the Mayor himself."

"You may be right," said Ira thoughtfully, "but we will soon find out."

"How?"

"Wait a minute. Bert must just tell me a little bit more."

Turning to Bert he said: "This Delrio is, then, a small fat man, has one gold tooth in his mouth and is the professional knife-thrower you mentioned?"

"Yes," said Bert steadily.

"When does he open his saloon?"

"It's always open."

Ira reflected.

"And you think it might have been him and not the Mayor."

"I do," said Bert, but Ira noticed the touch of caution in his voice.

"Good enough," he said. "Now I begin to know where we are. Joe and I will look at once into this Delrio."

"When's at once?" snapped Joe.

"Tonight," answered Ira with a delightfully disarming smile.

"Tonight!" shouted Joe. "What about today? Now? This very minute?"

"He's probably not up yet," was Ira's steady reply, "it's still only eight o'clock. No one plots anything at eight o'clock in the morning. Better to see him later tonight. I'm tired." He yawned suddenly. "Falling asleep in that chair did me no good. No good at all."

"Well, it's your own damned silly fault," said Joe warmly. "That there patience game of yours does get on my nerves. Anybody would fall asleep over that."

The manager was getting impatient.

"Fight this out between your two selves," he said. "I must get over and see how many cattle we've lost. Do you want anything more from me, Sheriff?"

"Just one small thing," said Ira.

"What's that?" said Bert sharply.

"Are there any ranches *over* the border of this State? Your plans," he explained, "only cover this State itself."

The manager smiled.

"The nearest one is the Valley ranch, which is just over the border due east of Station Six. Then there's the Morgan ranch due west of Station Eleven, and then the Morton ranch. That's a very big one, almost as big as this, but a good hundred miles away to the north."

"How far over the border are the Valley and Morgan ranches?"

"About ten miles each."

"I see," said Ira thoughtfully. "And who owns them?"

"I just don't know," said Bert. "I've never had time to find out, but from what I hear in the town a wealthy man bought both of these ranches a few years ago."

"Who's the man?"

"I just don't know, Sheriff: and does it matter anyway?"

"Not much probably," confessed Ira. "But do you know his name?"

"I believe that I've heard that he's a Mister Phillips, but nobody in this State knows anything about him or has ever seen him. He lives, it is said, in New York and the ranches are run by managers."

"Not much help there then," said Ira, sitting thoughtfully back in his chair.

The manager turned to go but suddenly halted.

"Didn't you tell these two boys of yours to go to bed last night? What *were* they doing running round this ranch this morning?"

Ira said smoothly: "Plain blank disobedience to orders. That's all."

He looked at Joe.

"Isn't that right?"

Joe looked at Ed and grinned.

"Well, you see, Ed and me was yarning. We weren't really tired, and Ed said to me, 'Here, let's have a ride round.'"

185

"And, of course," said Ira accusingly, "you said 'Yes'. But don't put the blame on Ed, you old rascal. I don't believe that it was Ed who suggested the ride round. I think it was you. Am I right, Ed?"

Ed blushed but said nothing.

Ira looked at him and smiled. "What were you yarning about?"

Ed blushed but again said nothing.

"Okay, Ed. Forget it. Off you go, Bert."

"How did they get to Stations One, Two, Three and Four?" Bert's voice still sounded suspicious.

"Joe can only count up to four," laughed Ira.

"Ira, you're a damned liar!" shouted Joe. "I can count up to at least——" He was counting hard on his fingers.

"I'm off," said the manager, glancing hurriedly round him, "*and now*."

He banged out of the room.

Ira watched the door being shut.

"Joe," he said, "I do wish you wouldn't talk so much. Why did you try to mention that dead Chink at the ford?"

"Dead Chink!" said Joe. "How the hell did you know that?"

"Saw his body," said Ira laconically.

"You saw?" gasped Joe.

"Shut up," said Ira. "Someone's coming, I think."

"Ed," he said, "tell me quick. Was there a tear on Buck's sleeve?"

"No," said Ed, "there wasn't."

"Right, Ed," said Ira. "Off you go and have a little sleep: and when Buck's ready, go out with him wherever he wants to go; but be in the saloon at nine tonight."

"Thanks," said Ed, as he left the room.

"I could do with a little shut-eye myself," said Joe." He looked tired. "I am not as young, Ira, as I used to be."

"Sorry, Joe. No shut-eye for you. You're off now to the Valley ranch the manager has just mentioned."

"Okay, you old slave-driver. What do I look for?"

"Branded XIT cattle."

"I've got you," grinned Joe. All the tiredness had gone from his face.

"You'll be back by about four. Then your turn of shut-eye and then the saloon—at nine-thirty."

"You said nine for Ed."

"Nine-thirty for *you*. Get me?"

"Delrio," said Joe softly. "You've got that hunch too?"

"Maybe," answered Ira non-committally. "When did you have it?"

"Hours ago," said Joe contemptuously. "Ira, you're getting a bit slow in your old age."

"Scram," laughed Ira. "I'm sure someone's coming."

Joe lingered.

"That Chink?"

"Never mind the Chink. Bring this" (he handed Joe a sealed envelope) "to the saloon with you; and pretend to be a little bit drunk when you arrive."

Joe began to grin.

"Scram!" said Ira fiercely. "Somebody *is* coming."

Joe scrammed—and just in time. The Mayor came in.

"Where's everybody?" he said. His face looked anxious.

"Anything worrying you?" asked Ira.

"Yes, there's a rumour down town that there was a raid at Station Six last night and that Buck's been killed. Do you know anything? Has Buck been killed? And where's Bert?" The questions reeled one after the other off his rather white lips.

"Sit down, Mayor," said Ira. "I can tell you everything. There *was* a raid last night—and at Station Six. Buck was not killed but *is* wounded."

"Seriously?"

"Fortunately, no. Just a knife-graze in the arm."

"Knife-graze?" said the Mayor in a high, startled voice. "Did you say knife-graze?"

"I did," said Ira, and went smoothly on. "But he'll be all right. He's resting upstairs now and will have nothing worse than a stiff arm for a day or two."

The Mayor seemed to relax.

"What happened?"

"Buck had gone to Six and then gone on to Eleven. On his way back to Six he met a stampede of cattle. Couldn't do anything by himself, of course; so let the cattle go and waited for the men driving them. There were about twenty of them. One of them knifed him. That's all."

"Did he recognize any of them?"

"No. They were all masked."

The Mayor's eyes travelled round the room.

"Where's Bert?" he asked.

"Just gone off to see how many cattle are missing."

The Mayor sat back. Behind his thick glasses it was impossible to detect the expression in his eyes, but he seemed to be thinking.

"Sheriff," he said suddenly. "This is dreadful. Last night was the seventh raid in ten consecutive nights, and we still haven't the slightest clue. What *are* we going to do?"

"Keep waiting and hoping," said Ira. "These mavericks—or the man behind them—will make a mistake some time—sooner or later."

"That would be cold comfort," said the Mayor, "if Buck *had* been killed."

"That little bit," said Ira, "interests me. How did this rumour start that Buck had been killed?"

"I don't know," confessed the Mayor. "I got it from that fellow Delrio who runs the saloon. He always," he added bitterly, "seems to know everything, and"—with sudden passion in his voice—"if I could close that damned saloon of his—it's a complete plague spot, Sheriff—I'd do so tomorrow. But," he remembered suddenly, "how do you know anything of him? We didn't mention him to you last night."

"Bert did this morning."

"Good," said the Mayor. "You look tired yourself, Ira. Been out all night?"

"Nothing so daring," said Ira shamefacedly. "I started to play patience and fell asleep before the fire—a silly thing to do at my age. My old bones are now aching like anything."

"Better be careful, Ira," laughed the Mayor. "I've never heard of a death from playing patience yet, but you never know."

He got up to go. Ira was looking out of the window. "Wait," he said. "Here's Bert back, and it looks from his face like bad news."

The manager came in. He scarcely glanced at the Mayor or even, for that matter, at Ira, but just went straight to his chair and slumped heavily into it.

The other two men eyed him with concern.

"What's wrong now?" asked Ira.

"Anything new?" asked the Mayor eagerly.

"Nothing *new*," answered Bert, "but four hundred head of cattle went last night. More than I thought, and the biggest loss we have ever had yet. If this goes on, I'll be fired—and damn pronto, too."

His face was strained and anxious.

"For God's sake, Ira, do something, but do it quick."

Ira's answer was sharp.

"I *can* do something now. Four hundred cattle just don't disappear into the blue in a few hours. Where the devil are they? You two must know this country better than me. Where can four hundred tired cattle be hidden? And, I suppose," he added, before either of the others could answer, "these cattle were all branded."

Bert said dully: "All our cattle *are* branded, but that has never helped us to find them yet; and, if I knew where they could disappear to, I would have found the place myself by now."

"So would I," said the Mayor.

Ira lit his pipe, very slowly and deliberately.

"Well," he drawled, "I've been studying these plans. If I had stolen four hundred head of cattle, I *might* take them to that gorge there" (stubbing the plans with his finger). Both looked at the point he had indicated.

"Impossible," shouted Bert. "There are miles and miles of dense scrub, no water, no shade. Cattle could never live there. We've both thought of that before, haven't we, Mayor? But it just won't work."

"We have," replied the Mayor, "but I agree with Bert. I don't think that the cattle are anywhere near the Blackwater Gorge."

"Well, we'll see," said Ira. "Joe's just gone there."

The simple statement seemed to electrify both men. "What!" they gasped simultaneously.

"Joe's just gone there," repeated Ira, and his voice was very smooth and silky as he added: "He left about an hour ago."

Bert got to his feet.

"*You* know, Sheriff, what you're doing, but it seems a wild-goose chase to me. However, get on with it. I've got to pay the men at Station Twenty-one."

The Mayor was looking very oddly at both Ira and Bert.

"But you don't generally pay the men on Thursdays," he said to Bert.

"Not generally," growled the manager, "but there has been some trouble there recently, and I want to go and check it up for myself; so I am making the excuse of paying them today and hearing what their complaints are. Coming, Mayor?"

"Yes," said the Mayor. "We all seem to be working today, so I might as well do the same thing. My office must be full of callers by now—all demanding loudly to know why the Mayor's late."

He smiled at Ira.

"All working, that is, except our patience-playing Sheriff. Isn't that it, Ira?" The smile that accompanied the words robbed them of any offence. Ira took no offence and smiled back. "I get a lot of relaxation from playing patience," he said.

The other two went off. The house was utterly quiet, so that only Ira heard the little timid knock of the small Chinese girl.

CHAPTER III

It was three o'clock in the afternoon, and the hot sun was beating down relentlessly on the arid waste of desert that stretched for miles on all sides of the Blackwater Gorge. In winter the Blackwater River could be a raging torrent, but now it was nothing but a thin trickling lazy stream.

The watcher who (for some two hours past) had been surveying the desolate scene from behind a convenient boulder began to feel anxious. Had something gone wrong? Was nothing going to happen after all? Was it worth waiting any longer?

He decided to go, but before he went he took one last look round and his heart jumped. In the far distance some object was moving slowly along what seemed to be a small trail. Hastily whipping out a pair of powerful field-glasses, the watcher examined the object. It was revealed as a man on a horse. From the distance the man seemed to be rather heavily built and not very tall. He was wearing a black mask, and as the watcher watched, he dismounted and carefully took cover behind a thick clump of cactus that bordered the trail.

The watcher smiled to himself and grimly pulled out his gun.

He fired six shots in rapid succession. He was too far from the man to be able to hit him and he knew it. But the shots had the effect that he had intended. As the sound of them reverberated round the rocky walls of the gorge, the man darted out from his shelter, mounted his horse and rode furiously away.

The watcher, through his field-glasses, studied the retreating figures of man and horse, but as he did so, a puzzled frown suddenly showed on his face.

He pondered for a few minutes, and then himself rode off in the opposite direction, but, as he did so, the puzzled frown became deeper. He had expected to see the sort of man he had seen but not a grey horse.

CHAPTER IV

Joe reached the office about four o'clock in a very tired and surly mood.

"Of all the damn fool jobs to give me," he shouted at Ira the minute he saw him, "riding to that damn fool ranch for nothing at all. What in hell, Ira, are you up to?"

Ira was sitting drinking a cup of coffee and staring at his cards. "What did you find?"

"Not a damn thing, Ira," Joe growled. "Did you expect anything?"

"There might have been something," said Ira defensively and rather evasively. "You never can tell."

He pricked his ears intently. "Joe," he said, "I think that that's Buck stirring. Off to bed. Quick."

Joe was so tired that he made no attempt to protest.

"Quietly," said Ira, "and tell Ed not to tell Buck you're back."

Joe tiptoed out.

Ten minutes or so later Ed and Buck came into the room.

"Feeling better, Buck?" said Ira.

"Much better, thanks." He glanced at the cards. "Still playing that damn silly game of yours."

"How's the arm?" asked Ira affably.

"Fine, thanks." He looked round the room. "Where's Joe?"

"Up at the Blackwater Gorge. He went there this afternoon but hasn't come back yet."

"Blackwater Gorge?" gasped Buck. "What the hell's he doing there?"

"He had a hunch. Joe gets hunches from time to time, you know, and always backs his own hunches."

"But that's the damnedest silliest hunch I've ever heard of," laughed Buck loudly. "What in tarnation did he ever expect to find there?"

"Don't know," said Ira laconically. "Maybe missing cattle."

"In that desert? Don't be silly. Cattle wouldn't live there for a day."

"Well, it doesn't matter," said Ira mildly, looking at his cards. "He'll tell us when he comes back."

He became absorbed in the cards.

Buck watched him for a minute or two.

"God help us," he said suddenly. "What a way to pass your time when there's work to do. Come on, Ed. Let's go."

"Station Twelve, isn't it, Buck?" said Ed eagerly.

"Station Twelve it is, son."

"Expect anything?" queried Ed with eyes bright with excitement.

"Never know," said Buck laconically.

Ira said to Ed: "Tell Buck about nine o'clock."

They left the room. With a puzzled frown on his face, Ira turned again to his cards.

"You're slipping, Ira," he said gently to himself. "You haven't got any real clues yet; and, what's more, you know it: and it won't be long now till somebody starts calling your bluff —and in earnest."

He filled his pipe and started to meditate; but, in two seconds, Bert came in.

He was tired, dusty and travel-stained. He had obviously ridden far during the day, and was, equally obviously, in almost as bad a temper as Joe had been. He glowered at Ira.

"Can't you stop playing that silly game, and get something done? Honestly, I don't think you're pulling your weight on this. The owners asked you to come here and help us, but so far you've done nothing. Nothing," he added bitterly, "at all. Ira, this just isn't good enough."

Ira said nothing.

192

As usual there were some odd blacks that Ira hadn't been able to fit in . . .

"Oh, for God's sake, talk," snarled the manager irritably. "Where's Buck?"

"Station Twelve. Just left."

"And Ed?"

"Gone with him."

"And Joe?"

"Not yet back from the Blackwater Gorge."

"Ira, if you don't mind my saying so, that's the silliest thing you ever did. You're just wasting everyone's time. There's absolutely nothing there."

"It was Joe's own hunch—not mine," lied Ira. "My hunch is this Delrio fellow"

This answer put the manager into a little better humour.

"You think then that it's Delrio, do you, Ira?"

"Well," said Ira carefully, "I don't really think it was the other."

"Nor I, either," said the manager. "The Mayor is the most honourable man for miles around here. It is really unthinkable that it was *him*."

"But you must confess," said Ira, still very carefully, "that it just *could* have been him. It was you yourself who first suspected him, wasn't it?"

His eyes were cold and steady as he looked at the manager and continued: "You see, Bert, these raids must have been planned by someone who had knowledge of the working arrangements of this ranch. Someone who knew where your reserve force would be at any one time, and someone, therefore, who struck at the places where the reserve force wasn't. You and Buck have that knowledge, I know, because you've both just told me so. But I suspect that the Mayor might somehow have got hold of it too. Am I right?"

Bert faltered.

"You *are* right. Buck doesn't know this. But I myself had thought that there might be a possible inside angle to this. I trust Buck, but it did look as if somebody were giving away information. So I mentioned it to the Mayor, and he asked me to let him know the movements of the reserve force, so that he might keep an eye on what was happening and possibly discover something for me that would help."

"I understand," said Ira. He was about to say something

more when the Mayor himself came in. The Mayor was just as tired and travel-stained as the manager himself.

"Did you fix Station Twenty-one, Bert?" he asked.

"Of course," said the manager, throwing him a very surly look.

"There's a rumour in the town that, in the raid last night, a Chinaman was killed."

"Well, what of it?" said Ira, abruptly. "This, I suppose, is just another of Delrio's rumours, and I pay little attention to them. Anyway"—he rose—"I'll be seeing that gentleman myself at nine o'clock tonight.

He began to walk out of the room.

"Where are you going?" said Bert.

"For a ride round to clear my head."

"Meet me in the saloon at nine o'clock," he added as he left the office.

The two men stared at each other.

"This beats me," said the manager heavily.

"Me too," said the Mayor. "But, if everybody has gone, you may as well come down to my place and have something to eat before we get to the saloon."

"May as well," said Bert.

They went to the stable and mounted their horses. Ira's was already gone: but before Ira had left he had noticed (with a curious smile on his face) the other two horses in the stable and the initials on the saddle of the grey one and the few cactus prickles that were still adhering to its fetlocks.

CHAPTER V

A Chinaman—a small, old Chinaman with a sad, worried face— was behind the bar of the saloon as Ira entered it just before nine o'clock.

"Gentleman want?" asked the Chinaman.

"A small rye," replied Ira.

The Chinaman gave it to him. Ira carefully took it to a table in the far corner of the bar, and sat down and pulled out his patience cards. The Chinaman's eyes were riveted on him.

Ira started playing. The room was empty and very quiet.

The Chinaman was suddenly standing over Ira.

Ira had seen his quick move from behind the bar, but had pretended to take no notice. The Chinaman, with his eyes as black as coal, demanded fiercely:

"You Sheriff Ira?"

"Yes," said Ira.

"You avenge Ching?"

"Yes," said Ira.

"Little Lee all right?"

"Yes," said Ira. "Little Lee perfectly all right, Chung."

Chung looked at Ira for a moment.

"How did you know that I am Chung?"

"Little Lee told me. She's a lovely child."

Chung relaxed.

"She is my only blossom now."

"And a very nice blossom too," said Ira. "Where's Delrio?"

"Coming, I think," whispered Chung as he darted back again behind the bar.

Delrio came in.

He was small, squat, fat and swarthy.

"Good evening, Sheriff," he said, but with a slightly mocking smile round his lips as he said it. As he smiled the gold tooth in his right upper jaw was very obvious.

"Evening," grunted Ira, "but how did you know I'm a sheriff?"

"In this bar," he replied, "I hear everything and see everything."

"And know everything?" said Ira.

"Nearly everything," answered the other. The expression on his face was so smooth and oily that Ira (who had disliked him on sight) felt very inclined to punch him on the jaw. But he just said:

"Okay. Tell me what you know."

Delrio looked at him contemptuously.

"I know, for instance," he said "that there's a sheriff here who never rides anywhere, never does anything and never finds out anything."

Ira felt, under this insult, an even stronger desire to punch Delrio on the jaw, but he just answered smoothly (though with a touch of indignant colour over his cheek-bones): "What else do you know?"

Delrio leered.

"See that gold tooth?" he asked. "Did anyone tell you that a professional knife-thrower with one gold tooth in his mouth knifed Buck last night?"

Ira's voice was very calm and steady as he replied: "Yes, someone did."

"I guessed so," leered Delrio.

"What an ugly-looking devil he is," thought Ira to himself as his eyes travelled slowly upwards from the badly shaven jaw he had so much wished to punch to the great mole on Delrio's forehead.

"And was it by any chance," said Delrio angrily, "our beloved Mister Phillips?"

Ira's heart jumped and nearly missed a beat, but his face was taut and tense as he replied:

"And who is this beloved Mister Phillips?"

"That's the one thing," said Delrio "that I just don't know. He runs everything, Sheriff, in this state—just everything. He robs, he murders, he pillages—just does whatever he likes. He steals—whatever he likes. Even names."

"Even names?" gasped the astonished Ira.

"Even names." The expression on Delrio's face was so strange that Ira suddenly wondered if the man were mad. He looked at his cards.

As usual, there were some odd blacks that Ira hadn't been able to fit in—the two of spades, the four of clubs, the ten of clubs and the ace of spades.

Ira scarcely heard the whizz of the knife that shot behind his ear and landed quivering on the ace of spades.

Delrio grinned.

"There's your Mr. Phillips."

Ira said: "Fun's fun, but that knife might have killed me."

"A professional knife-thrower aims to kill—or to miss, Mr. Sheriff. That knife was aimed to kill Mr. Phillips and to miss our beloved Sheriff."

"I see," said Ira thoughtfully. But his mind was working very fast.

"But who *did* tell you of the man with the gold tooth?" demanded Delrio fiercely.

196

"*Not* Mr. Phillips," said Ira firmly. "I've never met him and I've never seen him, so far as I know; but I will probably meet him some day."

"Good," said Delrio savagely, "and I hope I'll be there when you meet him."

"That knife of yours, Delrio, won't leave that ace till I've found him. I'll guarantee you that."

"Customers coming," said Chung.

It looked as if Delrio would have liked to say something more, but he went back behind the bar to greet his customers.

The customers were Ed and Buck.

"Anything doing?" asked Ira.

"Not a thing," retorted Buck. "Nothing ever happens at this time of day, and nothing ever happens anyway in saloon bars." His face was twitching, and Ira realized how true it was that the head cowboy was on the verge of a nervous breakdown.

"Have a drink," he said softly.

"I don't want any of your damned drinks," shouted Buck. "Why the hell have you brought us here? I'm telling you there'll be another raid tonight while we all stand about listening to your damn silly nattering."

"Shut up, Buck," said Ed.

"Good advice," sneered Delrio. "Got over your wound quickly, didn't you, Buck?"

Buck leapt for Delrio. Delrio didn't move, and Buck stopped short just before he would have reached him.

"You swine," he said, as he sat down panting beside Ed.

Delrio pursued his advantage. "Skin grazed, wasn't it?"

Buck said nothing.

"Anyone that *can* throw a knife," continued Delrio contemptuously, "doesn't throw it to graze skin. He throws"—his black beady eyes darted at Ira—"either to kill or to miss. That right, Sheriff?"

Ira yawned and answered: "I suppose so."

Buck glared at Delrio but still said nothing. Ed touched Buck's shoulder. Ira gazed abstractedly at Delrio.

"What are you thinking of, Ira?" said Ed.

"Names," said Ira very shortly.

There was a sudden interruption. The swing doors of the saloon opened and the persons who now entered were the

Mayor and the manager. They glanced round the saloon, saw Ira and sat down beside him.

"Why did we have to come here, Ira?" Bert said. "We're both tired. What earthly good is this going to do?"

Before Ira could answer, Delrio cackled: "Either of you seen Mr. Phillips today?"

"What's he talking about?" said the manager wearily.

"*You* know," answered Delrio with the ugliest smile on any human being's face that Ira had ever seen.

"Go on," laughed Delrio, stridently and loudly. "You're all here—managers, cowboys, mayors and sheriffs. Now our Sheriff's going to find Mr. Phillips."

"We're not all here," said the Mayor. "Where's Joe?"

Before Ira could answer, the saloon door opened again. This time the new-comers were six in number—all tall and sun-tanned and in spite of their ordinary clothes, somehow giving an indefinable impression of authority.

Their leader ordered six small ryes: and they all sat down together with the ryes that Chung had obediently served them.

Through lowered eyelids Ira saw the quick glances that were darted at them by everyone in the saloon and noticed the sudden stiffening of Buck's jaw, the equally sudden pallor on the manager's lips and the deliberation with which the Mayor took off his spectacles, wiped them and slowly put them back on his nose.

Delrio's face had, however, not changed in the least. The ugly sneer was still round his lips

"What," he said, "are we all waiting for now?"

"Joe, I expect," answered the Mayor.

"And Joe," sneered Delrio, "is just about to walk in, bringing Mr. Phillips with him and say 'Sheriff, here's your Mister Phillips.'"

"Which is exactly," said Joe as he banged through the saloon door, "what I am not going to do."

Joe was in a tremendous temper.

"You're Delrio, I suppose. Give me a drink, quick."

"Courtesy," snarled Delrio, "costs nothing."

"Which is less than what your lousy drink will cost. Let's have it before I shoot this dump up."

"What the hell's wrong with you, Joe?" shouted Ira. "Have you been drinking?"

"Mr. Sheriff Aten," replied Joe in a rather unsteady voice. "I don't like that fellow's face; and, when I don't like a face, I just don't like a face. Here's something for you."

He handed to Ira an envelope, and sat down heavily in his chair.

"Joe's drunk," said the Mayor.

"Who gave you that?" asked Ira quietly.

"Find out," said Joe rudely as he suddenly fell asleep.

"He *is* drunk," said the manager.

"Drunk as a coot," sneered Delrio. "Our beloved Sheriff's act has failed, and we're no further forward. You may all just as well go home, and the State Troopers can go with you too. No arrests tonight, and no Mr. Phillips, and everything will just go on as before."

"State Troopers?" gasped Buck.

"Be your age," rapped Delrio. "These are State Troopers, even though they're not in uniform. Anyone would spot them at once. I spotted them, and so did all of you, and you know it."

As his accusing eyes swept round the room no one answered except Ira.

"They are State Troopers," said Ira.

"And who brought them here?" asked Delrio.

"I did," said Ira.

"And where's Mr. Phillips? Did you bring him too?"

"That's my business," said Ira. He turned towards the leader of the State Troopers.

"Lieutenant Gilmour, have you anything for me?"

"This," said the Lieutenant as he handed over a sheet of closely printed paper.

Delrio practically doubled up with laughter.

"Patience, drunks, envelopes and now bits of paper, but never Mr. Phillips. Never—no, never—Mr. Phillips."

"Shut up," said Ira, very sharply. "You"—pointing to the knife on the ace of spades—"have had your professional act. Now I'm having mine."

"And a damned poor act it'll be, I bet."

Lieutenant Gilmour calmly covered Delrio with his gun.

"The Sheriff said: 'Shut up'. So shut up".

Delrio's face was twitching.

"Okay," he said, "let's all sit back and enjoy the big act. Start, maestro! Characters in order of appearance. Who's your first character?"

Ira picked up the two of clubs and placed it on the three of diamonds.

"Buck," he said, "why did you cut your own arm?" His voice was quite gentle, but Buck gave no answer. Ira continued: "The sleeve of your shirt was *not* torn, and you would scarcely have been riding in the middle of the night with your sleeves rolled up, would you?"

Buck looked helplessly at Ira, and in a toneless voice said: "So you know, do you?"

"I think so, but tell us. Now's your chance to do so."

"Do you believe," demanded Buck hotly, "that I ever had anything to do with these raids?"

"I do not."

"Not?"

"Not."

"You mean that?"

Delrio sneered, but Ira answered: "I do mean that. Tell us, Buck."

Buck began to laugh—a thin, high-pitched, hysterical laugh that ended in a kind of choking sob.

"Thank God, thank God."

He rose to his feet and the words were tumbling out of his mouth. "Okay, I'll speak."

"Carry on," said Ira.

"Well, you're right. I *did* cut my own arm. These raids were obviously planned by someone who had inside knowledge of the ranch's working. I felt that everybody, including him"—he gestured towards the manager—"*and you* suspected me. Remember what you said the night you arrived. You asked me if I *knew* that anything was going to happen. Ira, I just didn't." His voice broke. "I went to Station Six, as I've told you, and then to Station Eleven, and when the stampede occurred I just——"

"Lay in the ditch?" said Ira.

"You're right," said Buck, very quietly. "There was nothing I could do to stop that stampede, so I just did lie down in that

200

ditch. The head cowboy," he said bitterly, "just did lie down in that ditch and just cried."

"But did the head cowboy," said Ira, still very gently, "see anyone?"

"I saw exactly what I told you, except that no one threw a knife at me."

"Ira," said the Mayor unexpectedly, "Buck's been suffering great strain for months. He told us a very silly story, but I understand what he felt. Ira, you are not going to punish him, are you?"

"Well," said Ira heavily, "lies are lies and they throw suspicion on other people."

"Forget the other people," said the Mayor. "I'm one of them, I know; but Buck's a sick man. What he said doesn't matter to me. Delrio, does it matter to you?"

Before Delrio could answer, Ira said (and very sharply indeed):

"The point is that it may matter to *me*; and if you gentlemen would leave me to attend to my own business we might all get on a bit quicker."

"Sorry," said the Mayor, "rebuke accepted."

Delrio said nothing, but his eyes were hot with anger as he glared at the Mayor.

"Buck," said Ira, "that *was* very silly of you. But you're no criminal. Ed, take him off to bed. Let him stay there for five days; and, while he's there, you'll be the head cowboy in his place."

Ed blushed. Ira put the two of spades on to the three of hearts.

"Manager not being consulted on this?" asked Bert. His face looked very old and weary as he said it.

Ira felt a twinge of compassion as he answered very curtly: "No. There'll be a new manager of that ranch after tonight. Go on, Ed, take Buck away."

Buck and Ed left.

The manager kept looking at Ira with very dull eyes.

After Ed and Buck had gone he said: "So you know about me too then, Ira?"

"I think so," replied Ira, moving the four of clubs on to the five of hearts. "I've already told you that this has always looked like an inside job to me. There were only two 'insiders' who could have given information away. There was Buck, for one; but he didn't, so that only leaves you."

"What about the third?" said the manager bleakly, with the look of a hunted animal on his face.

"The one you said was the third," retorted Ira brutally. "He's here. We'll ask him. Mayor, did Bert ever tell you where the reserve force was?"

"Never, Ira."

"Did you ever ask him to do so?"

"Never." His voice had a ring of sincerity in it that convinced everyone.

"I accept that statement," said Ira curtly. "You lied to me, Bert, and you know it. How could the Mayor have helped to stop these raids? How could he have discovered anything? We all know that he has no authority over this ranch. He has only two or three men under his control. What could he possibly have done?"

Bert said nothing, but his face was more like a hunted animal's than ever.

"And whose grey horse," pursued Ira's relentless voice, "was at the Blackwater Gorge this afternoon, and who was waiting there to kill Joe when Joe arrived there?"

The manager dropped his head on to his hands.

"Very well, Ira. There's nothing for it but the truth, the whole truth and nothing but the truth." He conjured up a wry smile. "That should please the Mayor as he represents the law. But how *did* you know that I was at the gorge this afternoon?"

"Saw you and your grey horse," said Ira brutally. "Fired six shots at you. Saw your grey horse again in the stable an hour ago, and there were still cactus prickles on his fetlocks. Go on. come clean."

The manager's face was drawn and miserable.

"Okay, I will. Ira, I'm a gambler, and I used to come down here and join"—motioning to Delrio—"in that swine's poker parties."

"You're a liar!" yelled Delrio.

The manager disregarded the interruption and went evenly on.

"I kept on losing, and in the end I owed Delrio a thousand

dollars. That's a lot, Ira, for a man like me; and I couldn't find the money to pay it."

"Why didn't you ask me?" said the Mayor.

"I just couldn't," was Bert's reply. "How could I?" He looked at Ira and repeated: "Could I?"

"I don't know," answered Ira very flatly. "I'm not here to answer questions. What happened next?"

"Well, Delrio began to press me for his money. He said it wasn't his money but Mr. Phillips's money."

"That's true," shouted Delrio. "It *was* Mr. Phillips's money."

"Then why did you say just now," demanded Ira, "that Bert was lying about the gambling parties?"

Delrio swore under his breath, but gave no answer.

"Go on," said Ira.

"He told me that Phillips would expose me unless I gave him certain information for passing on to Phillips. Certain information. That's all. You can guess the rest. And," he added, "I've always known that the stolen cattle were sometimes driven to that gorge for a night or two before going on somewhere else. There's a small clearing behind it where cattle can easily shelter."

"I saw that clearing today," said Ira grimly. "but there were no cattle there when I saw it, although there were plenty of signs that cattle *had* been there only a few hours before. So, I suppose, you went there to kill Joe before he could discover anything?"

"Not to kill," said Bert miserably. "Just to watch. Why should I kill Joe? If he had found anything, I just meant to disappear."

"I don't believe you," said Ira savagely. "If *I* hadn't been there you *would* have killed Joe to save your own skin. Take him away, Lieutenant, and charge him with being an aider and abettor in the theft of the cows stolen from the ranch. We can't charge him with attempted murder, though I very much wish we could."

Two of the Troopers led Bert away.

There was a moment's silence after his departure. Ira picked up the ten of clubs and held it questioningly in his hand.

"One more to be fitted in," said the Mayor.

"But not Mr. Phillips, I'll bet," snarled Delrio.

"Wait and see," said Ira, "it might be either Mr. Phillips or the murderer of the Chinese labourer called Ching whose dead body was lying in the ford near Station Four last night."

Delrio's face went very white.

Chung suddenly moved from behind the bar to join the group of men and stood impassively behind Delrio.

"How do you know," blurted Delrio, "that anyone *murdered* this Ching?"

"Someone saw him being murdered," was Ira's steady answer.

Delrio licked dry lips. "Prove it," he shouted.

"Bring in Lee," said Ira abruptly.

One of the Troopers brought in a small Chinese girl. Her frightened eyes looked round the room, but before she could say or do anything there was a knife in Delrio's hand, poised ready to throw. That knife, however, never left Delrio's hand: another knife went through his shoulder-blades.

"Justice is done," said Chung. "Arrest me, Sheriff, if you want to."

"Take little Lee away first," rapped Ira.

The trooper took her away.

"Lee," said Ira, "saw the person who murdered Ching, and that person was this worm Delrio. Why he did it I do not know."

"I'll tell you," snarled the dying man. "It was this Ching that gave me my orders from Mr. Phillips. He had told me that I had to meet him last night—on urgent business and at Station Four. I went there." His breath was coming heavily and painfully. "When I got there he said that Phillips was going to have me arrested for a lot of murders, and that he was to give evidence against me. So——"

"So?" said Ira.

"I killed him." His head began to sag. "I killed him," he repeated in a loud, shrill voice, "but who is this Phillips that goes everywhere and does just what he likes?"

His head fell back.

"He's dead," said Gilmour.

"Damn good riddance too," said Joe, half waking up.

"May I go now?" asked Chung. "Or do you arrest me?"

"How *can* I arrest you?" said Ira. "What have you done to justify my arresting you?"

"Knife in Delrio's back," answered Chung primly. "Not usual procedure." His wooden face almost smiled.

"Not *very* usual," agreed Ira, "but it's not usual either to have a man hurling knives at a child; so that I think that the child's grandfather was quite entitled to knife the man that tried to knife his grandchild. Do you agree, Gilmour?"

The Lieutenant quickly said that he agreed.

"Then can I go?" asked Chung. "Little Lee needs comforting."

"Wait, Chung," said Ira, "just for two or three minutes more. I think we are now going to discover Mr. Phillips."

"Gilmour," he rapped, "have you found out who that dead rat lying there really is?"

"It's all, sir, in that paper that I handed to you a few minutes ago. That paper comes from the records of the State Department, and is only available to official authorities. Read it, sir."

Ira began to read it. Joe was watching him very carefully.

With a touch of vague discomfiture that he couldn't explain to himself, Ira was conscious of Joe's eyes as he read: but when he'd finished reading he merely said:

"Yes, it is all here. Listen."

" 'Delrio was born in Chicago forty-six years ago, the son of hard-working and honest parents called Phillips.' "

"Phillips!" said the Mayor in a startled voice.

"Phillips," repeated Ira shortly. He continued reading.

" 'The boy took to evil courses, and in 1845 in the State of Ohio knifed a man called Meridith and killed him. Then he escaped into Louisiana where once again he killed a man called Willoughby—and in the same way: but once again managed to escape. This time he went to Illinois and there killed a man called Delrio. He then came to this State and very cleverly (it threw the State Department off the scent for quite a long time) called himself Delrio.' "

Ira stopped reading.

The Mayor said: "I really must congratulate you, Ira. This is a grand job of work you've done, and this town will be more wholesome as the result of it. Bert (the thief), the murderer of Ching and Mr. Phillips all fixed up in twenty-four hours of patience playing. You don't really play patience," he said teasingly. "You only pretend to."

Ira said: "I *do* play patience." He put the ten of clubs on the jack of hearts.

"That's them all gone," laughed the Mayor.

"Not all," said Ira. "There's this one." He pointed to the ace of spades still lying under Delrio's knife. "I have got to deal with him, haven't I, Mayor?"

"I don't get this, Ira," said the Mayor irritably. "You've found everybody, even including Mr. Phillips. Who are you after now?"

"The *other* Mr. Phillips," said Ira very grimly indeed. "The *real* Mr. Phillips. The brain behind all this."

"But there isn't any other Mr. Phillips."

"There is," said Ira. "There's the man who knew Delrio's real name and Delrio's history of murder after murder; and the man who thought that, by calling himself Phillips, he was providing an alibi for himself."

The Mayor polished his spectacles.

"I see," he said softly. Banteringly he added: "Ira, in my view, you go from strength to strength. Who is this other Mr. Phillips?"

"He might be in this room right here and now," was Ira's answer.

"But not a State Trooper?" joked the Mayor.

"Not a State Trooper."

"Then who? There's only me, you, Chung and Joe left, and it can't be you; and, surely, it can't be poor old Joe."

"Less of that poor old Joe stuff," said Joe indignantly.

"Sheriff, can I go now?" asked Chung.

"No," rapped the Mayor, "you can't."

"Why not?" asked Ira.

"Because," said the Mayor significantly, "if there *is* another Mr. Phillips it's as much my job as yours to find out who he is. I am an officer of the law, and I would like to ask some questions, if I may."

"From whom?" asked Ira doubtfully.

"That Chinaman."

Ira's face cleared.

"Okay; carry on, Mayor."

"Ching," said the Mayor: "was your son, wasn't he, Chung?"

"He was," said Chung.

206

"And how did Ching happen to know that Delrio had committed murder after murder?"

"Mr. Phillips had told him so," was Chung's reply.

"And who is Mr. Phillips?"

"I don't know," answered Chung.

"Did you know that Delrio's real name was Phillips?"

Chung hesitated.

"Answer the question," rapped Ira. His gun was cocked.

Chung looked at Ira impassively.

"I *did* know," he said, folding his arms.

"And how," sneered the Mayor, "did you happen to know that?"

"Ching told me."

"And how did Ching know?"

"Mr. Phillips told *him*."

"And you don't know who Mr. Phillips is?"

"I don't."

"That's all," said the Mayor abruptly. "Ira," he whispered, "send Chung out for a moment."

"Chung," said Ira, "would you just nip out and see how that horse of mine is getting on?"

Chung walked out.

"There's your other Mr. Phillips," said the Mayor. "Knows everything—everything! And not because Ching told him, or Phillips told Ching; but because he himself *is* Phillips. That's right, isn't it, Ira?"

"Could be," said Ira thoughtfully.

"But, Mayor," he added slowly. "You know the processes of the law better than I do. Don't we need just a little more proof?"

"Proof! But what sort of proof? He's confessed everything, hasn't he?"

"This sort of proof," said Ira, opening the envelope that Joe had given him.

The Mayor craned his neck to see it, but Ira kept it in his hand.

"What is it?" asked the Mayor.

"The message Ching wrote out as he was dying and gave to little Lee. How Joe got hold of it, I just don't know."

"And I'm not telling," snapped Joe. Ira looked levelly at him.

Chung came back in.

"Horse all right, Sheriff."

"Read that," said Ira, handing the piece of paper he had taken out of the envelope to Chung. "Read it. Read everything it says there." His voice was very hard and cold.

All eyes were fixed on Chung.

"I don't get this," said the Mayor.

"Never mind," answered Ira swiftly. "Watch Chung, and watch him as hard as you can." Ira's gun was still cocked.

Chung was helplessly turning over in his hands the piece of paper.

"Read it," shouted Ira angrily. "What does it say? Tell me, what does it say?"

The Chinaman looked sadly at Ira.

"I don't know."

"Why not?"

"I can't read."

"Can't read?"

"No, Sheriff. Neither could Ching; and Ching couldn't write either, and neither can I."

"Let me see that bit of paper," said the Mayor steadily.

Chung handed it to the Mayor.

The Mayor read it aloud. The words were: "Five thousand dollars reward if you just say that Mr. Phillips is Joe."

"So it is Joe, is it?" sneered the Mayor.

"No, it dam' well isn't," snarled Joe, as he leapt to his feet, furiously bellowing at Ira: "What the hell's this? Are you trying to railroad me?"

"I'm not trying to railroad anyone," said Ira shortly; "but I have been trying to find the real Phillips, and now I'm certain it isn't Chung. Chung clearly can't read. Otherwise he would have known what that paper said. So it must be true that his knowledge of Delrio's past must have come from what he had been told and not from what he had read, and the person who told him could only be a person who could read."

"I don't quite agree," said the Mayor. "There are other possibilities, Ira."

"None that matter," said Ira crossly, "Delrio's past was known only to Delrio and to these State files. Delrio didn't give it away, but the files would—to anybody who could get at them and read them."

"Not necessarily officials?" said the Mayor.

"Not necessarily officials," answered Ira gloomily, "just anyone who, if and when they see a file, can read it."

"But you said a minute ago," said the Mayor, "that you thought that the real Mister Phillips might be in this room now."

"I did," said Ira, "because, frankly, I had rather suspected Chung. Joe can't read." Joe threw Ira a very curious look and began to smile. Ira looked at him anxiously but continued, "Which would leave only you and me. Both impossible. So that, Mayor, I've just failed in my main quest." He began to pick up his cards.

"Sorry, Ira," said the Mayor gruffly. "I understand your disappointment. But you really have done wonders so far, and there are other days to come; and I bet you'll find your other Mr. Phillips yet."

"Maybe," said Ira. "But you see, Mayor, I just hate to be beaten. I've done everything I could. Last night I myself rode out and found that dead Chink. Joe found him too, but that must have been later than me, because when I was there little Lee was weeping over Ching's dead body. She told me she had seen the man that had murdered Ching, and described him. It was Delrio—and no one else," he added significantly, "because Delrio has a mole under his right eye that you haven't got."

"Thank God for that," said the Mayor heartily, "otherwise——"

Ira completed the sentence.

"Otherwise you would have been the chief suspect. You see, from the moment I arrived here, Bert seized every chance he could to throw suspicion on you—but in a subtle and very clever way. He told me of the *two* men with the one gold tooth each; but, as he told me, he was all the time cunningly trying to direct my mind towards *you* and away from Delrio, though in his actual words he said the exact opposite."

"He was a poker player," said the Mayor, "and not a patience player like you."

"I sometimes play poker myself," said Ira gently, "and I think I know a bluff when I see one. But, anyway, let me go on. He then told me that you knew the movements of the reserve force.

I just didn't believe that, as you now know. It didn't seem to make any sense to me. Why should you have *asked* for that information? What good could you have done with it? You, as Mayor, had no men that could have helped."

"You're dead right."

Ira held up a warning finger.

"But at the same time, Bert was also trying to put suspicion on Buck; and, for a bit, I'll tell you quite frankly, Mayor, I *did* suspect Buck too. All along I've felt that these raids must, to some extent at least, have been an inside job, so I tried to follow Buck last night. I didn't quite know where he would go to, but I guessed either Six or Eleven. I went to Eleven first: then back by Four where I saw Ching. Then to Six but, as I got there the stampede was on: and then everything *did* happen, so far as Buck is concerned, just exactly as he has described it and as I myself saw it. But when he started telling that cock-and-bull story this morning, I got Ed to look at his sleeve. It was just possible that somebody might have tried to knife him afterwards, but the sleeve proved otherwise and you know the rest."

"But why were you so clear, Ira, that *he* never gave any information away? I'm sure you're right, but just satisfy my curiosity."

"Buck, as you yourself were the first to point out, is obviously a sick man. And the rest is simple psychology. If Buck had given the game away, would he have been near Station Six at all? Wouldn't he have kept as far away from it as possible, just in case something might go wrong and he himself might get caught? And if, for any reason that's beyond me, he was there *because* he had given the game away, what in hell's name is the point of just lying in a ditch and crying?"

"Good psychology," said the Mayor approvingly. "But then it *was* true that there were about twenty men driving these cattle?"

"Of course it was."

"With one small fat one with a gold tooth?" smiled the Mayor.

"That I just do not know," answered Ira. "That's Buck's story, but the men all passed *me* so rapidly that I couldn't see any of them."

"Right, go on, Ira," said the Mayor. "What else have you done today? You're an old rascal, you know. Every one of us thought that you were just playing patience, but you seem to have been getting round as well. Blackwater Gorge this afternoon. Tell me about that."

"Well," said Ira with a grin, "I lied about that of course. Joe never went there at all, but I gambled that any guilty person who thought that Joe was going there and who *knew that something might be found there* would be there too. So I went there and waited; and the guilty person did arrive. Mayor"—he laughed suddenly—"when I first saw him, I thought for the moment that it was you."

"Me!" said the startled Mayor.

"Well, you and Bert are both about the same build, though he's a bit taller than you, and he was a good mile away when I first saw him. But——"

"But?"

"But I didn't know which of you rode a grey horse. So I checked in the stable when I went out this afternoon. The grey horse wasn't yours, Mayor. It did have cactus prickles still in its fetlocks, but its saddle had the initials A.J."

"A.J.?"

"Albert, otherwise Bert, Johnson."

The Mayor's eyes were gleaming with excitement.

"This is the best story, Ira, I've heard in years. Go on. What in the devil's name did you do next?"

"Well, this Mr. Phillips has always interested me. It was Bert who first told me he owned these two ranches over the border, and I had a hunch that one or other of these two ranches might supply the answer to my problems. Cattle must go somewhere, mustn't they?"

"I agree," said the Mayor, "but I only wish I knew where."

"Well, Joe went to the Valley ranch, and what did you find there?"

Joe's answer was very surly.

"Nothing at all. An old woman of eighty, and six cows just about as old as herself."

The Mayor reflected. "By the way," he said, "who wrote that bit of paper? If Ching couldn't write who did write it?"

"Me," said Ira. "You see, Mayor, that was a trap. A trap to catch the other Mr. Phillips, but a trap that unfortunately misfired."

"I'm going home," shouted Joe suddenly.

He got up.

Ira sat still.

Joe sat down again.

"Just one more question, you old rascal before we go," said the Mayor to Ira. "You haven't yet *fully* accounted for your day. What else happened this afternoon?"

"Well," said Ira slowly, "I went over the border to the State of New Mexico. There I saw these Troopers and asked them some questions, the answers to which you also now know."

"The Delrio questions?"

"That's it," said Ira.

"And anywhere else? Now, Ira, don't hold out on me. My instinct tells me you did go somewhere else."

So far as Ira could blush, he blushed.

"You're right, Mayor, I did. I went to the Morgan ranch as well. It's only five miles from the clearing."

"Find anything?" queried the Mayor eagerly.

"Yes," answered Ira. "Four hundred branded XIT cattle."

The Mayor whistled. "I'm just beginning to understand this. So, from the gorge, they get driven over to this Morgan ranch and then——"

"Into anywhere in the United States that Mr. Phillips wishes. He's smart, is that Mr. Phillips, and I think," said Ira sorrowfully, "just a shade too smart for me."

"Nobody, Ira, will ever be too smart for you. You'll get him in the end. Surely you got some kind of line on him at the ranch itself?"

"That's the infuriating part of it. Nothing really concrete or definite. I of course questioned the head ranchman about how the cows had got there. He's a shifty, evasive sort of fellow and claimed he knew nothing at all. And I think that's true, because the procedure seems to be that about an hour or two before each raid three or four men arrive at the ranch—all masked, of course. They come on Mr. Phillips's orders, and lock the resident staff into their own quarters. The cattle are then driven into the ranch after the raid by other men while the staff is still locked up. All the men then go, unlocking the staff; and, after the hue and cry has died down, orders are received from New

York to send the cattle in small groups to various places all over America where the XIT branding means nothing at all to anybody. So that"—Ira jabbed his finger at the Mayor—"no one there has ever seen any of the raiders and no one has ever seen Mr. Phillips either, though I think it's as plain as a pike-staff that he himself must get to that ranch sometime or other during the raids, if only just to see what's happened."

"Of course he must," snarled Joe. "Only a plain goddam fool wouldn't want to know that everything was hunky dory, and this Phillips ain't no fool; and, Ira, you ain't caught him, and you won't catch him by talking. So let's go."

He got up.

"I agree with Joe," said the Mayor, also getting up. "There can't be much more left to tell."

"Only," began Ira, "one other little thing."

"Oh, forget it," yelled Joe, "there's always one other little thing with you; and it never adds up to anything anyway. I'm off."

"What's this one other little thing?" asked the Mayor.

Ira got up.

"No, I think Joe's maybe right." He was looking very curiously at Joe. "Perhaps it wouldn't add up. Let's go."

He began to pull on his gloves. So did Joe. Ira was watching Joe intently. The Mayor felt in his pockets and began to walk towards the door. Ira was watching him equally intently.

"It's cold tonight, Mayor. Aren't you putting your gloves on?" asked Ira.

"Not so cold as all that," laughed the Mayor, "but I'll do anything to please you, Ira." He pulled out a glove and put it slowly on to his left hand.

"Nice glove," said Ira. "Where's the other?"

The Mayor felt again in his pockets. "Must have left it at home," he said shortly.

"Or at the Morgan ranch, perhaps?" said Ira suddenly.

"And what, Mr. Sheriff Aten, would you mean by that?" said the Mayor in a very hard and steady voice. His right hand was still in his pocket.

"The one other little thing—that I've just mentioned. Here it is." He threw on the table a right-hand glove identical with the Mayor's other glove. "Found," he said carefully, "at the

Morgan ranch this afternoon. Dropped, I should think, by the Mr. Phillips who——"

As the Mayor's hand came out of his pocket Joe fired, and the knife that was meant for his heart dropped harmlessly on to the floor.

"And that's that," said Ira as he put the ace of spades on the king of diamonds. He looked at the dead man. "Mayor Gallagher—the only man in this State who had access to official documents and could there read that Delrio's real name was Phillips. The man who bought the two ranches, calling himself Phillips as an alibi for the future. The man who, when Bert got entangled in gambling debts to Delrio, used Delrio to find out from Bert everything that he wanted to know about the XIT ranch. The man whom Delrio could never discover, the small fat man that *was*, I think, leading the drive of those cattle last night; and, thank God, the small fat man who did drop that glove at the Morgan ranch this afternoon."

"Well, that's all over," said Ira, "and we can all now go home. Coming, Gilmour? Coming, Joe?"

"Yes, sir," said Gilmour.

"But no, sirree," said Joe.

Both men looked at him in amazement. Joe was on his feet, holding his gun directly pointed at Ira's head. There was a very ugly look on his face, and his voice was very cold and menacing as he said: "Not yet, Mr. Sheriff Aten. All is not over. *You* have had *your* fun: your mysteries: your bits of paper. But now I am having my fun."

Gilmour made a quick movement towards him.

"Stand back," roared Joe.

"Better stand back, Gilmour," said Ira. His face looked white and drawn. "I think Joe's gone mad."

Joe laughed—a harsh discordant laugh.

"Joe hasn't," he sneered, "but Joe knows as many tricks as even Sheriffs do. Particularly, Ira, dirty ones."

Gilmour stirred again.

"If you don't want to get shot, Gilmour," said Joe, "don't move a muscle till I've finished speaking."

He looked ferociously at Ira.

"The real Mister Phillips is a man that can read, isn't he? The Mayor could read, so the clever Sheriff has pinned everything

214

on to him. But the clever Sheriff could have seen these files and the clever Sheriff can read. And . . ."

Gilmour gasped as a horrid suspicion crossed his mind.

"Beginning to see what I mean, Gilmour?" said Joe softly.

All the colour had drained out of Ira's face.

"I know," continued Joe, "a big rat when I see one. " The emphasis on the words "big rat" was enormous. "And I would like our Sheriff to read that."

He hurled at Ira a piece of paper. Ira glanced at it. The expression on his face was indescribable.

"Read it!" yelled Joe.

Ira's face twitched. "Okay, I'll read it."

"Every single word," snarled Joe.

"Every single word," said Ira.

He began to read. His voice was completely flat and toneless.

"The big rat bit the cat."

"Dead right," snarled Joe. "Go on."

"And the cat bit the big rat." Ira paused.

"Go on!" yelled Joe. "What's the next word?"

All the colour had returned to Ira's face. With a very broad smile on his lips he solemnly answered:

"Back."

"That," said Joe, grinning as he lowered his gun, "was exactly my own hunch; and my hunches are always right, aren't they? You wouldn't have caught that Mayor but for my hunch, would you?"

"No," said Ira solemnly, "I wouldn't."

Joe preened himself.

"From now on, Ira, just you follow my hunches and talk less. You're too fond of talking. That's your trouble."

Ira laughed.

"Maybe," he said, "but what's all this about dirty tricks and big rats?"

Joe was abashed.

"Well, it *was* a dirty trick to tell everybody that I can't read."

"But you can't!" said the astonished Ira.

"And that," said Joe with a rather coy smile on his face, "is just where you're dead wrong. I can. Ed's been teaching me. I know all the three-letter words, but it was a dirty trick of Ed's to put in a four-letter word at the end, wasn't it?"

"It was," said Ira.

Joe grinned—a very happy grin. "How's it spelt?"

"B-A-C-K."

"B-A-C-K," repeated Joe carefully, "when I get BACK I'll tell that young Ed off, good and plenty."

"I bet you will," said Ira.

Joe glared at him.

"It will do Ed good," said Ira pacifically. "That young man is just getting a little bit uppish. Let's go."

They went.

YOU HAVE FOUND WHAT
YOU WERE SEEKING

The moon shone brilliantly on the snow-clad peaks; and the waters racing down the valley gleamed like silver. Beneath the great fir trees stood the tepees of the Arapaho Indians. Down by the banks of the river their allies, the Cheyenne Redskins, had their own encampment. Neither tribe had had time to erect their totem poles; the camps had been built hastily two days before.

Shortly after two in the morning clouds blew up from the west. The Cheyenne sentry posted on the water's edge yawned. Danger was past: the moon was covered up and it looked like snowing. He had spent the hours of his guard peering across the river to where a horse track came out of the mountains. Two days previously his fellow braves had crossed the ranges by this track. Tired and thirsty, they had camped by the river, and now each family was asleep. More than a hundred children lay quietly in papooses by their mother's side.

The guard yawned again. It was a weary business keeping one's eyes fixed on one point. He would go and have a word with Summer Rain, the guard posted by the Arapaho up by the woods. Perhaps his colleague had built himself a fire in the

217

shelter of the forest. It was bitterly cold; he would like to stretch out his hands in front of a fire.

Summer Rain had been told to keep watch from the upper branches of a tree, but when the clouds had come up he had decided that there was no point staying sixty feet above the ground when he could only see a few feet ahead of him in the inky blackness. He had just jumped down on the carpet of pine needles when he heard the low whistle which the Indians used as a password. It was Wild Horse, the Cheyenne sentry.

The idea of building a fire appealed to Summer Rain. He knew a clearing in the forest where they could safely heap up the pine needles to make a fire. Together they set to the task. The flames danced round the edge of the pile of needles and then with a roar the whole bonfire took light.

"These needles are cracking loudly tonight," commented Wild Horse, stretching out his numbed hands.

"They are very dry," replied Summer Rain.

"Stop," hissed Wild Horse, "listen!"

The cracks were not only coming from the fire: they were coming up from the river.

"Guns! Paleface!" shouted Wild Horse.

The two men dashed to the tents of the sleeping Arapaho. But already the braves were awake, seizing their bows and spears.

Wild Horse did not wait. He rushed across the sloping fields towards the river. The guns were still firing, but now louder than the shots were the yells and shrieks of the wounded. It was too late to do more than save the women and children—to put up a fight while they could make for the cover of the woods behind.

Wild Horse ran to the tent where his wife and children were sleeping. He opened the flap. Two American soldiers were just about to leave.

"The only good Indian is a dead one," one was saying to the other.

As they ducked to come out of the tepee Wild Horse brought his tomahawk down on their heads, one after the other, and the two whiteskins rolled on to the ground. But he was too late to save his family.

Colonel John Chivington had led his force of U.S. soldiers across the mountains in pursuit of the fleeing Redskins. Two hours previously he had halted at the very point where the track came out of the rocks into the valley. The moonlight was too bright to risk an attack. But when the clouds had blown over the moon Chivington waved his men forward. Quietly they had tiptoed down to the water's edge, and there they had upturned the canoes that they were carrying. In five minutes the first party had paddled across, letting the fast current carry them along, only using the paddles to guide the canoes.

The raiding party wasted no time. They looked for the sentry, and, finding none, had set to work running from tent to tent killing the braves before they had time to snatch their arms. Fearing that the squaws would give the alarm to the other encampment, the soldiers exceeded their orders and put a bullet through every sleeping body.

Wild Horse shouted his tribe's battle-cry. If any of his kinsmen were left to fight, they would take up the cry. One or two calls came out of the darkness, but they were not the full-blooded roars of a Cheyenne in arms, they were the weak calls of defiance from a few last braves lingering between this world and the next.

It was too late to do anything. His family lay murdered. His fellow braves were either dead or dying. He too must die in battle, for death was the only fit punishment for a sentry who had deserted his post.

Perhaps the Arapaho had had enough time to prepare, he thought, as he raced back towards the woods. But, no! The shots of guns were already ringing out. The bonfire left unattended had spread to the surrounding trees, and now a belt of wood was blazing like the fires of hell. In this wild light the shadows of the fighting men swept across the grass like the beams of a black searchlight.

It was man for man and life for life. If the Indians could fight off the Americans before their reinforcements came across the river they might have a chance to escape back into the forest. Wild Horse threw himself into the fight. Picking up the spear of a dead Indian, he lunged into his enemies. Then he felt a sharp pain in the side of his head. Quickly he put up his hand: the blood was pouring down his cheek. A bullet had gone clean through his ear; another inch one way and it would have gone through his brain.

The squaws were picking up their children and running from the battle.

"At least some will be saved," thought Wild Horse, plunging back into the fight.

A bugle call announced the arrival of American reinforcements. The soldiers in the first raiding party broke off the fight and ran to join the ranks of the main body. The Americans, falling on one knee, levelled their muskets and fired off volleys into the Indian camp.

Another bugle call and the line of soldiers started to advance with fixed bayonets. From the camp a drum was being beaten. Wild Horse stopped to listen.

"Retreat to the woods!" came the message from the drum. Wild Horse turned round to look at the woods: the wall of trees behind was aflame. The other side of the flames was safety. But how deep went the fire?

There was no time to consider. The Chief's order was to be obeyed. Wild Horse tore off his clothes lest they should catch light. Naked he sped into the blaze. The flames licked his skin. He could feel nothing but the intense pain on his feet as they fell on the carpet of burning pine needles. Half delirious with the agony, he raced on. Then all of a sudden he struck a belt of air so cold that it seemed that he had fallen into a freezing river. He had passed the belt of fire. But the shock of the change of temperature was too much for him; his sturdy body crumpled and pitched on to the ground.

That night the Americans killed more than 500 of the 650 Redskins camped by the waters of Sand Creek. Of the Cheyenne, except for the sentry Wild Horse, not one man, woman or child escaped. The Arapaho women were more fortunate. They took to their heels in time to skirt the forest fire and reach the woods beyond. But of their menfolk those who were not killed in battle mostly died in the fiery inferno. Only those who, like Wild Horse, stripped to the skin survived, and of these the total was twelve.

The cold light of morning woke the survivors to their senses. They set out to look for the women who had run for shelter deeper into the woods. It took a long time to round them up; they had scattered in small groups for greater safety.

* * * * *

Only a week earlier the two tribes of Cheyenne and Arapaho, short of food, had surrendered peacefully to the American outpost at Fort Lyon. The garrison commander had accepted their surrender, but had then turned them away, saying that he had no food or quarters to spare. It was then late in November 1864, and the snows already covered the mountains. Silently, despondently, the Indians turned away from Fort Lyon and started back into the mountains.

For the last two years marauding parties of Americans had come riding into Cheyenne country, shooting the great herds of buffaloes. Wherever they rode, they shot the animals. If they did not need them to eat or for their skins, they shot them for target practice; and the black carcasses of buffaloes littered the valley slopes. For untold centuries buffaloes had met every need of the Redskins. Their meat nourished, their skins clothed them; the squaws wore moccasins of buffalo hides on their feet, their tents were filled with utensils made from their bones. Now with the coming of the white man their source of food was being denied to them. They consulted their medicine men, and the advice which they received was to surrender to the white man.

This they had done. They had trekked two hundred miles to the nearest fort, they had begged the commander to help them, for they had not enough food to last the winter. And all they had received was a promise that, if the Americans received supplies from the east, then the garrison commander would send on a few mule loads of rice to the Indians. It was for this mule-train that Wild Horse was watching as he tried to keep himself warm by the banks of the river.

True, one or two of the braves suspected danger. As they tramped back from Fort Lyon these doubting ones pointed to the coldness shown by the Americans. If they had wanted to be our friends, surely they would have invited us to sit round a fire with them, they argued. But they kept us waiting outside the gates of the fort as if we were infected with disease.

"Trust not these palefaces. Their pale blue eyes hide deep cunning," said the oldest of the braves.

But even the most cynical Redskin never suspected that the Americans planned to massacre them all. The Indians did not know that beneath the rock of the lands where they lived and hunted were fabulous deposits of gold. The White Man knew.

221

He had not come into the Indian country just to shoot buffalo; he had come to prospect for yellow riches. And when he had found what he was looking for, his eyes narrowed with greed, and he determined to kill those who stood between him and wealth—to kill the Redskin braves, the hunters of the Cheyenne and the Arapaho.

Wild Horse gathered the squaws and children in a clearing in the woods. Everywhere the air was filled with the bitter smell of burning. The women cried, the children whimpered for food. The men went off to the camps to see what food could be found in the devastation. That night they lit a great fire by the banks of the river and there paid honour to the dead.

"Vengeance on the white traitors!" shouted Wild Horse.

"Death to those who do not honour the rules of war!" cried another.

"Death to those who fight dishonourably!" roared a third.

"Death! Death!" screamed the women.

"Death! Death!" chorused the orphaned children.

Wild Horse seized a drum found lying in one of the tents. With frenzy he started to beat out a message. Bumpti-bumpti-bum-bum-bum! Bang-bang-bum! Bang-bang-bum! The sharp beats swept through the air and raced on up to the mountainsides, which threw them back as echoes. Quicker and quicker beat the drum until its message overtook the returning echoes. The valley filled up with sound and like a saucepan boiling up with milk suddenly overflowed, and the din poured out across into the next valley, and the next, and the next.

On mountain-tops, by water's edge, in the deep forests and on the hot sands of the south, Redskins stopped in their paces and listened. The message from Sand Creek was relayed from drum to drum across the whole Wild West. "White Man's cunning. Red Man dead. Red Man chop off White Man's head."

Wild Horse led the survivors of the massacre away into the mountains of Montana. Among the Arapaho children was one who had never known his father. His mother had been married to a French trader, but the Frenchman had been gone for over four years; he had returned to France with a train-load of furs. The little half-caste boy had the perky, upturned nose of his father and the long, fast legs of his mother's race. His mother called him Jean after her departed husband, but the rest of the

222

tribe called him "Frog" after his father's favourite kind of food.

Wild Horse was especially fond of Frog; he was the brightest of all the Arapaho children who survived the Sand Creek massacre. Wild Horse taught him how to shoot an arrow to hit a buffalo eye a hundred yards away. He taught him how to hurl arrows, how to rip off a scalp with a tomahawk, how to fell a man silently with a knife between his ribs. When he was eight years old he was a trained soldier. But Wild Horse had more to teach him.

One day Wild Horse came up to Frog leading two ponies.

"Jump on, Frog," he said cheerfully. "We are off."

"Off where?" inquired Frog, putting down his bow and arrow on a nearby boulder.

"Don't ask so many questions, you inquisitive rascal. Run to your mother's tepee. You will find that she has a bundle wrapped up for you."

Like an arrow shot from his taut bow, Frog raced down the little street of buffalo-skin tents.

"What's this talk of Wild Horse, Mother?" He stood just inside the tent panting from the run.

"Come here, child," his mother said tenderly. "Bend down and let me put this over your head." Gently she lifted the golden thread from around her neck and placed it over his head so that the golden cross rested in the centre of his chest.

"Take this, Jean, my darling!" The tears came to mist her eyes as she spoke. "Take this with all my love. Your father gave it to me on the day we were married. He had always worn it and his father before him."

"But what does it do?" asked Jean, squinting down coyly at the cross.

"It will bring you much luck. I know not what it means, but to your father it was very precious. When you reach the White Men they will honour you for wearing such a necklace."

"When I reach the White Men," repeated Jean incredulously.

"Jump to it, Frog." Wild Horse's gently spoken command sounded from outside the tent.

"Mother!" shouted the boy in alarm. "What is all this about?"

But his mother would not tell him. Wild Horse would reveal

223

all that was necessary on the journey. His mother beckoned him to her.

"Let me kiss you, dearest one. You will be a grown man and I an old woman before you come back."

Jean bent down to be kissed, because he was already tall for eight years old, and his mother was squatting on the floor.

Nearly a month later Wild Horse and Frog approached the valley of the Missouri. There, where the river is still swirling with icy water down from the mountains, the White Men had built a town. As soon as Wild Horse saw the chimney-stacks in the distance, he reined in his pony.

"Here is where we say good-bye," he called to Frog.

The youngster no longer asked questions. He knew what was required of him. Wild Horse took off his saddle the bag of little yellow nuggets that he had specially collected for Frog.

"You see how the White Man's eyes pop out when you show them these," he said, handing over the bag. "Keep care of them: they will have to last you a long time."

The two tribesmen, the old one and the youngster, bade a ceremonial good-bye. They bowed and each put his hand over his nose. They repeated the "Song of Parting", the Indians' pledge of eternal friendship. They turned their backs on each other: Wild Horse rode back to the mountains; Frog led his pony timidly towards the new pitch-pine buildings of Pierre, capital of South Dakota.

Wild Horse returned to the Arapaho encampment. Though a Cheyenne himself, he was accepted by the Arapahos, for in all things he excelled. He was a fast runner, a brilliant marksman and as brave a fighter as any. But what made him most popular with the Arapaho was his way with the youngsters. He gave all his spare time to teaching the growing boys the arts of hunting and of war.

One day he led a dozen of the boys out into the darkness. He explained to them: "I shall go off into the forest. After a while I shall move quietly towards the camp. Your job is to stop me. You must try to find me, and then when one of you has spotted me, he must give the call, and all the others must run and join him in stopping me."

The boys searched, but without success. They combed the forest, but Wild Horse had completely disappeared. After a

*The two tribesmen, the old one and the young one, bade a
ceremonial good-bye*

time they got hungry. After twenty-four hours one after another drifted back into the camp. They went to sleep, but when they woke up the next morning there was no sign of Wild Horse. They waited a day for him. Then they went to the Chief to tell him that they were worried.

"A bear may have attacked him," they suggested.

"He may have caught his leg in a hole and broken it."

"Or he may have been set upon and killed by palefaces."

The Chief was worried, too. It was not like Wild Horse, the most skilled of fighters, to get lost. He ordered his attendant to beat the drum. When the tribe had come together, he ordered all the men and boys to pack up food and follow him out into the woods to search for Wild Horse.

For two days and two nights they combed the woods. They shouted, they lit beacon fires, they split up into groups, but nowhere was there the least trace of Wild Horse.

Then the snow started to fall. It was useless to go on with the search. The Chief ordered the men back to the camp, and the boys were pleased at the prospect of a hot meal and a sleep inside a tent, though deep down inside each of them felt something missing, for Wild Horse was gone and they would never see him again.

Imagine their surprise—Wild Horse was waiting for them by the totem pole when they returned.

"A fine bunch of boys you are!" he mocked at them. "I have occupied this camp and killed all your mothers and sisters."

For a moment they thought that he had gone off his head, so loud were his peals of hollow laughter. The Chief rushed up to him, holding his spear ready to thrust.

"So, you Cheyenne scoundrel, this was a trick to tempt us from the camp, to give you a chance to have arrow practice on the Arapaho women. You shall be burned for this, you vile wretch!"

"Keep your temper, Big Voice." Wild Horse raised his hand. "Your women and children are in their tents preparing a nice hot meal for you. They will be delighted to see you. They have been laughing their eyes out."

Was he mad? Just then several of the squaws came from the tents. They explained that Wild Horse had returned to the camp a few hours ago, but had stopped them sending out a message to bring back the men and boys. He told them that the boys had got to learn to become scouts the hard way.

Big Voice threw down his spear. It was all right after all.

"Yes, you scallywags," said Wild Horse, pointing his finger at a group of rather sheepish-looking boys. "Your stupidity would have lost all your families. The White Man would have found the camp undefended and you would have returned to find your sisters all dead." He wagged his finger at them. "When I said I would return to the camp, you all thought that because I had no food with me, I would return before many hours had passed. But I have learned to live for a week without food and without moving. I climbed to the upper branches of a tree, settled down there and waited until the search party had walked by underneath. Then when the road was clear I simply walked back to the undefended camp."

The boys looked dumb with amazement. A whole week without food!

"All right! Back to sleep with you!" cried Wild Horse. "Tomorrow morning all boys report here and we will have another exercise in scouting."

"Huh! What's that? Sergeant!" The Colonel leaned forward on the desk. "Speak up, kid. I'm not having any clever-as-monkey pip-squeaks causing trouble in this city. What've you got to say for yourself?"

But it was no good asking questions of Frog: whether shouted, hissed or pleaded, he could not understand a word. In the end the Colonel's face went redder than his uniform.

"Take him off to the reverends!" he commanded the Sergeant.

Frog could not help laughing: the white men seemed to spend their day shouting at each other.

"Hi! Just a moment; lay down that bag, son. You couldn't have gotten that in any legitimate sort of way," the Sergeant shouted in the same tone as the Colonel had just used on himself.

Infuriated at getting no response, the sergeant tried snatching the bag from Frog's hand. But he had not bargained for the youngster having an iron grip. It took most of the headquarters staff of the U.S. 7th Engineers to winkle the bag out of Frog.

When Frog woke up he was looking out of a window at a big

226

building with a cross on its roof, a cross just the same shape as the one he had round his neck.

The Fathers of St. Anthony came from France; nothing so pleasant had occurred to them for a long while as the discovery that lithe young Frog spoke a few words of French. With real joy they undertook the task of bringing him up.

The monks were frankly disappointed that Frog, as he grew older, showed no signs of joining the Church. Whenever there was a spare moment the young Jean, as he was now called again, would rush off to the barracks. He proved as good a rifle marksman as he was with bow and arrow. The soldiers were very attached to him; they thought that he brought them luck. How could a lad who wandered in from nowhere without a word of an explanation carrying a bag of gold be anything but lucky?

When Jean was sixteen the selfsame Colonel who had shouted so gruffly (and who had confiscated the bag of gold) went across to St. Anthony's to have a word with the Prior.

"My men want him for a scout. The young feller speaks the Indian lingo as well as he now talks in English," the Colonel explained.

The Prior held up his hands fatalistically. "It is perhaps ordained. But I cannot help regretting that such a delightful youth should waste his life shooting."

"Waste!" The Colonel's voice lifted the ceiling. All of a sudden his eyes caught sight of a religious picture: remembering where he was, he said no more.

"He is yours, Colonel," the Prior added quickly before there could be another explosion. "I will send him down to the barracks tomorrow."

*　　　*　　　*　　　*　　　*

Wild Horse's fame as a trainer of young warriors spread with the years across all the Indian reserves. Chiefs of other tribes sent for him to train their lads in warfare. Sitting Bull, the famous and terrible medicine man of the Sioux, caused a instrument of heaven, the one sent from above to avenge the message to be beaten out proclaiming Wild Horse to be the Red Man.

Wild Horse had never been back to a Sioux encampment since

227

the massacre of Sand Creek. He feared for his life. This absolution from Sitting Bull came as a surprise to him. A simple man, he began to wonder whether perhaps he had not been sent to avenge the death of his fellow people.

As he passed down the line of tepees people would whisper: "He was spared at Sand Creek so that he might live to take revenge." Wild Horse smiled to himself. There was no talk that he was the one responsible for the tragedy by the banks of the river. Perhaps they did not know. Perhaps it was all his imagination. He smiled again to himself. Yes, he would be revenged in time.

That night he made a decision. When the village woke they found a message scrawled in the earth beneath the totem pole.

"HAVE GONE. COUNT NOT THE DAYS",

and beneath was a picture of a bow and arrow, which Wild Horse used as his sign.

He must see Frog. But how? He needed to find something first. It was lucky he knew where to find those little pieces of yellow stone which the white man so much valued. After a few weeks he had collected enough stone and dust to fill a moccasin (or, if he had known it, to buy up the main street of an American town). Then he tamed a mustang, a wild horse, and rode the beast across the rocky waste westwards. On the way white men forced him to give up his horse. They scoffed at him.

"Why should white men walk while a red nigger rides?"

Wild Horse said nothing, nor would he unless they put their thieving hands on the spare moccasin laced round his neck.

It was a weary journey trudging eastwards over the barren Dakota highlands; in the end he reached the spot where five years before he and Frog had said the "Song of Parting". This time Wild Horse went on into the city of Pierre, already grown twice in size since the last occasion he had looked at it.

But how to find Frog? If he asked too many questions the White Man would be suspicious. It was best to wait. He hired himself out as a building labourer chipping stone. Each evening he walked round the town, looking. He learned a little English. In time he could understand what the Whiteskins were saying to each other.

One evening he was standing in a saloon, pretending to drink, listening to a crowd of U.S. cavalrymen joking and swearing. Suddenly he pricked up his ears.

"Never seen a shot like that Red Indian kid in 'B' Troop," one of the troopers was saying.

"Yeah!" replied another. "Guess there's something screwy about that feller. He never misses a target. Kind of gives me the creeps."

That must be Frog, said Wild Horse to himself. So he had accomplished part of his mission. He could not contain himself any longer. Excitedly he nudged one of the soldiers' arms.

"Excuse, please. I the uncle of Red Man. Please, where he?"

"What's 'at?" The soldier was so amazed that he spilt his beer over the counter.

"I, uncle," was all that Wild Horse could get out in explanation.

"Ah, come off it!" The soldier to whom Frog gave the creeps elbowed him away. "You got no business interruptin' white folk."

Wild Horse felt the anger surge up inside of him. Sharply he bit his lip to hold back his fury.

"Please where?" he pleaded.

"Oh! Stop whining, big chief!" put in one of the men. "Your little nephey's gone north with the boys up to Bismarck. Get crackin' and go follow him."

Wild Horse did not need the last advice. He was gone almost before it was spoken.

Frog's troop of cavalry had been sent north a month previously to reinforce the northern territory. The countryside there had been terrorized by Indian raiders and white cattle thieves. The cavalrymen were ordered to halt and question suspicious characters.

Frog was riding his white mare, Swift Wind, over the bad lands, the rocky outcrops for which Dakota is renowned. As was usual, he was riding away ahead of the rest of the troop: he was the scout. So sharp were his eyes that he could spot a mountain lion a mile off. Often the other men in the troop would take bets on his eyesight.

"Bet you there's not a place where we can get a drink for fifty miles," one shouted.

"Give you two bucks there is."

"Done!"

"Tell you what," said the first, "we'll go and ride up to Jean and ask him which of us gets those two bucks. That kid can see as far as the North Pole."

And Jean put his hand up to his forehead to shield his eyes from the sun, scanned the horizon, and declared that there were a couple of farmsteads about twenty miles on.

"There, what did I tell you? I could smell liquor that far any day of the week. That'll cost you two bucks, Budge."

They let Jean get ahead of them. He was a smart kid. Let him take care of any odd Indian arrows that might be flying around; they would keep their skins safe for that drink.

Not more than ten minutes later an arrow lifted Frog's cap off his head, missing his scalp by a fraction of an inch. He pulled his horse up with a sharp jerk. How could he, the best scout in the cavalry, have missed that marksman? Doggone it! Another arrow kicked up the dust just a few inches from his left stirrup. Better dismount. No, better get out of here quick. He dug in his stirrups and reined Swift Wind off towards the only clump of trees in sight.

Whew! That was a close shave. Frog rubbed the sweat off his forehead. Just then there was a peal of laughter above his head. He looked up quickly. But, too late, the man had dropped down from the boughs straight athwart his horse, immediately behind him on the saddle. Swift Wind bucked her front legs in the air with the shock and bounded off. Frog struggled, but his arms were held in a tight grip by the attacker. He tried to get at his Bowie knife, but he was powerless. Who on earth? This was his number: he waited for the knife to plunge in his back.

The attacker kicked on the horse's haunches to bring her to a halt in a gulley of rocks. Then he spoke: spoke in the Arapaho language that Frog had never forgotten.

"Frog, you little fool, I never thought that you would let yourself be caught by that trick."

"Wild Horse!" Frog twisted round in the saddle now that his arms were free. "Wild Horse, why give me such a shock? Why not warn me that you were coming?"

"And warn the paleface?"

Frog nodded his head in understanding; then he threw his arms round Wild Horse's neck.

*   *   *   *   *

The door of the Commandant's office closed: General Custer was sitting in an arm-chair in the office of the Commandant of the North-Western Territory. Colonel Reynolds was there and a number of senior officers.

"Useful lad," was the General's comment.

"How does he get this information?" inquired the Colonel.

"Uses his eyes," said the lad's commanding officer. "The kid's got the eyes of an eagle."

"So the Redskins are massing round the Powder River." General Custer crushed his cigarette end on the floor with his cavalry boot. "Reynolds, take six troops of horse and see if you can get to the river before too many of them assemble. Read the Riot Act. Tell 'em to go home peacefully. Even give them some food if you like. But if they don't go, well, you know what to do, Colonel."

"Yes, sir." Reynolds was already on his feet examining the wall map.

"Better take that lad with you," Custer added.

"Yes, sir. I'll have him go ahead and warn the Sioux that Uncle Sam's going to have no nonsense."

"I'll follow up with the main force, Reynolds." Custer was ringing on the bell for an orderly. "But it will take me a week or two to muster all the men sent out on patrols and garrison duties."

The orderly stepped smartly to attention.

"Corporal," General Custer ordered in the voice that was feared up and down the U.S. Army, "have an order of general muster sent to every unit under my command. And have every officer commanding report here next Monday forenoon."

"Yessir!"

"And, Corporal, wire the White House that I'm moving into the field."

"Yessir!"

"And, Corporal, clean my gun."

The General strode out of the room.

231

Colonel Reynolds was well known throughout the West as a horseman and a horse-racer. He had even ridden at the horse shows in London and Dublin. Whenever there was a rodeo in a Western town Colonel Reynolds was sent for to give a display of riding, and the cowboys would yell their heads off for "the galloping Colonel". If ever a man could make a horse do what he wanted, even a wild, untamed horse—a mustang—it was Colonel Reynolds.

He wasted no time. Within forty-eight hours he was on the way to Powder River at a fast trot. Frog was given his orders; he was to ride out ahead and deliver General Custer's warning.

Frog was pleased. This was as he had wished. He delivered the message in his own way. He rode up to the camp of the Oglala Sioux and made straight for the Chief's tepee.

He bowed ceremoniously.

"Oh, great Chief," he said, "the white chief has sent me in peace to tell you that he commands you to surrender your women and children."

The Chief did not move an eyelid. He waited.

"Is that all your message?" he asked.

"That is what the great white chief commands," said Frog, standing his ground.

The Sioux Chief rose to his full height, his head-dress of feathers trailing over his shoulders down to the waist. "Then go tell your white master," he roared, "to come and fetch them in battle. Now, go!"

Frog bowed low and then dodged out of the tent. He smiled to himself as he mounted again on Swift Wind: his plan was working.

Colonel Reynolds received his scout's report while munching his lunch. He was a man of action. He threw away his chicken bone half eaten.

"Very well, Trooper," he said, rising to his feet, "you may return to your post. We shall teach Chief What's-his-name to live in peace and do as he is told, even if it means stringing him up on a tree to do it. We have treated him decently enough, telling him to go back home. Now, he'll learn the hard way. Orderly! Sound the bugle. We're moving off!"

The cavalrymen clambered into their saddles muttering complaints about the Colonel who would not let them finish their dinner. Reynolds detached the leading troop and ordered it to move round the right flank; the rear troop he sent round the left flank. His was classical generalship—take the enemy on all sides.

The success of this manœuvre depended on the enemy being taken by surprise. Reynolds was reckoning on the Sioux being caught right off guard: why, only an hour ago he had sent Frog with a friendly message telling them to pack off home.

Fleet Foot, the tall chief of the Oglala Sioux, was a canny warrior. He knew enough about fighting white men to know that the odds were heavily on the double out-flanking manœuvre being used against him. The way to handle this tactic was to out-flank the out-flankers. Scarcely had Frog left the village when he called the tribe together. Half an hour later he led the warriors out into the woods, leaving his encampment by the riverside to the women and children.

The U.S. cavalry carried out their manœuvre with the precision of a parade-ground exercise. Exactly at zero hour the right-flank force contacted the centre force and the left-flank party. One minute after zero hour the three combined opened a withering fire into the encampment. The women howled with pain: the babies screamed. Not a brave was in sight. Reynolds was a sportsman: he did not like the idea of firing at a sitting bird. He blew on his whistle and the shooting died down as suddenly as it had begun.

Reynolds dismounted. This needed looking into. Perhaps, after all, the Chief had thought better and decided to go off home. Then why leave the women here? This certainly was a mystery. Most of the men followed their Colonel's example of dismounting: they began to peer into the dark tepees.

This was Fleet Foot's moment. His men had gone an hour's march up to the rocky crest above the valley. They had waited and watched—watched the white cavalry wheel and come in to the attack. Then with a wave of the arm Fleet Foot sent his men speeding down the mountainside. The distance that had taken them an hour to climb was raced in ten minutes. In the brushwood behind the camp they jerked to a halt and took aim.

A shower of arrows fell upon the unsuspecting Americans. Reynolds felt for his revolver and fired in the general direction of the woods. But he could see nothing, and the next fall of arrows sent him running for shelter before he could take proper aim.

"Damn it!" he shouted, pulling his treasured horse after him. "These blighters laid an ambush for us. Dodge behind the tents and get on your bellies."

But his words did not carry across the tumult of shouting, cursing and desultory firing. Some of the cavalrymen mounted, some took shelter, some got down on one knee and started up a cannonade at the woods. Fleet Foot guessed that the Americans would be caught off balance. There was no chapter in the army tactics book about what to do when under a deluge of arrows coming from invisible bowmen.

With a savage yell Fleet Foot leapt out of the cover of the woods; brandishing his spear, he charged the White Man. His braves came running behind. How they shouted. It was as if they were seized by a frenzy. The horses neighed, reared and took fright. The riderless steeds bolted, knocking over anyone who came in their path.

Reynolds jumped on to his horse: an animal needs a master on top of him at such a time. He kicked in his heels and the horse charged forward in the direction of the oncoming Indians. He fired his Winchester as he rode. One brave fell, another tottered; and then he was through the line of oncoming braves, facing the empty woods.

It was too late to save the day. The charging Redskins terrified first the horses and then their riders. Reynolds wheeled his horse and galloped back through the attackers, but he was only in time to join his fleeing men. Shooting Indians was a good sport, but acting as their target did not appeal to the notions of the U.S. cavalrymen. They rode off as quick as they could.

*　　*　　*　　*　　*

While General Custer was shouting for his orderlies, Wild Horse was going about his preparations in a quieter but no less thorough way. His difficulties were greater than the White Man's. There was suspicion among the Redskin nations. Though they shared a common hatred of the white invaders, the quarrels between them were sometimes so deep that one side or other had been ready to stomach a temporary alliance with the White Man in order to get the better of his red foe. Rarely did more than one or two tribes gather together, and then it was usually to cement some alliance against another tribe.

Wild Horse went to see Sitting Bull. He was received with ceremony. For two days the tribe feasted and danced. Nothing was said. On the third night Sitting Bull took Wild Horse aside from the camp-fire.

"Why is it," Sitting Bull asked, "that our warriors are powerless against the guns of the White Man?"

Wild Horse replied: "We must use guns, too."

"No."

"Then we shall never be able to drive back the paleskins from our lands."

"There are other ways of winning in battle," Sitting Bull said with assurance, "ways which would be pleasing to our ancestors above."

"It is true that our departed fathers would not have us copy the White Man with his guns and his gin," Wild Horse replied, slowly thinking over each word. "But we have no other choice."

"We have to show to our braves that the gun is not to be feared," Sitting Bull declared.

"I wish that I knew how." Wild Horse settled down into his favourite squatting position.

"Listen," said Sitting Bull, starting to unfold his plan.

Next morning Wild Horse returned to the Arapaho encampment. A fortnight later the drums were beaten excitedly across the West. From tribe to tribe was carried the news that a prophet had arrived among the Sioux. Each tribe was invited to send two elders to hear the prophet's message.

When Wild Horse returned to Sitting Bull's encampment he knew what the prophet would say. But the other Indians were chattering with excitement. Not for many generations had such a prophet come to the Red Indians.

The elders of the nation were summoned to the top of a cliff. Waiting for them were Sitting Bull and other chiefs of the Sioux tribe. Sitting Bull called for silence. Suddenly, as if from nowhere, a tall Redskin in a white smock appeared in the centre of the crowd. He raised his arms and held them wide apart, like a scarecrow, as he spoke.

"Braves of the Indian nations," he intoned like a preacher, "your fathers have sent me to bring you their commands. You

have heard that the White Man has recently made an out-
rageous demand on our people: he ordered the Oglala Sioux to
give up to him their women and children. True to the spirit of
his ancestors, their chief, Fleet Foot, resisted and sent the
White Man fleeing whence he had come. He triumphed in
battle despite all the guns of the palefaces."

He paused for a moment to let the full effect of his words sink
in. His audience waited motionless.

"Your fathers bid you nations rise up in arms as one man and
fight the paleskins. You are to gather your people together by
the Little Bighorn River and build camp. You are to sharpen
your spears and tighten your bows. You shall show no mercy.
For as each white man is laid to the ground so shall one of your
fathers gain relief from his suffering in the world above. Until
the paleskins are driven back to the shores of the sea whence
they came your fathers cannot sleep or eat or drink. Rise up, ye
warriors. You are endowed with magical powers by your fathers.
You shall no longer be victims of the White Man's bullets. From
this day forth the bullets will pass through your bodies without
causing harm; for, so it is decreed."

Then, true to the magic of which he spoke, the prophet
vanished as suddenly as he had come. Before the elders had
time to discuss his words Sitting Bull started to address them.

"Braves. The prophet has brought us the message of our
fathers. Who is there among us who would not obey?"

In the silence that followed, the distant thunder of a storm
crashing into the Rocky Mountains echoed ominously.

"When the moon is next set let all you fighting men gather by
the Little Bighorn River. Now go. Make haste. Time is short."

*   *   *   *   *

Colonel Reynolds did not feel like making a personal report
to General Custer. He had enough imagination to guess that the
General's face would turn a colour that would make the most
lurid sunset seem pale. He decided to write a dispatch explaining
that he had been ambushed by superior numbers of Redskins;
that he had withdrawn to a protected position to wait for
the main force to come up. Frog was selected to carry the
dispatch.

The General was riding at the head of over a thousand men

when Frog cantered up and saluted. He handed over the letter and waited, trotting along by the General's side.

General Custer read the letter, and then he read it again. For the moment he betrayed no particular emotion.

"Trooper," he inquired, "how many of these Oglala Sioux were there?"

"Sir." Frog was not sure exactly how to reply. "It is hard to say. We never actually had time to see them. They caught us unawares."

"Trooper." The General's voice took on a sarcastic tone. "You were sent with Colonel Reynolds to be his scout. How come that your famous eyes missed these compatriots of yours?"

Frog blushed to the roots of his hair. What had the Colonel said in his letter? How much did he know? He started to stammer.

"But you see, sir."

"I don't see," shouted the General, giving way to his rising irritation. "And what is more, you didn't see, either. A fine scout you are. Get to the rear of the column and stay there. No, get back to Colonel Reynolds and tell him I'll reach his position in two marches. Get!" The General's face had gone that red-brick colour for which it was famous, and he was shouting at the top of his voice.

Frog did not need to be told twice.

As he rode westwards once more, Frog was thinking hard. How could he recover his reputation with the General? If he could only explain that Colonel Reynolds had been out-soldiered, but Custer would never listen long enough for him to get out the story. Besides, what was a trooper's word against a colonel's?

There was nothing particularly urgent about the message which he was carrying back to Colonel Reynolds. What if he made a detour? No one would know. Frog had decided that he would try to redeem himself in the General's eyes.

Before returning he rode fast across the flat country to the foot-hills covered with fir trees; dismounted for a quick drink from a mountain stream and then rode on again.

Colonel Reynolds was exercising his charger over a five-bar gate. He carried the gate round in the baggage train. Whenever there was a chance he had it taken out and set up.

"Well done, boy." He stroked the horse on its fine mane.

Frog pulled his Swift Wind to a halt and saluted.

"Red Indians, sir." The words came tumbling out. "Thousands and thousands of them. Gathering over the other side of the range by the Little Bighorn River."

"Is this a message from General Custer?" inquired the Colonel.

"No, sir!" Frog suddenly remembered the official message that he was meant to deliver. "The General's compliments, sir. He is on the way to join you. He will be here in two days' time. Please, sir, I saw the Red Indians myself. No one else knows about them."

Colonel Reynolds realized the peril of his position. If Frog's information was correct, he was hopelessly outnumbered. Apart from this inequality he did not fancy another battle lost: it did not help his chance of promotion. General Custer had better decide what to do.

"Look here, boy." He had made up his mind. "Grab something to eat and then get you back as quick as you can ride and tell General Custer exactly what you saw. Tell the General that, if attacked, I intend to disengage myself. I await his orders."

Frog snatched up a hunk of bread, filled his pockets with apples. His horse, Swift Wind, was less pleased at the prospect of riding back to meet General Custer than he was. The animal decided that a trot was quite fast enough, but his rider would have nothing less than a canter and brought down his whip until he got his way.

General George A. Custer had not yet recovered his temper even though twelve hours had passed since he had received the disagreeable news of Colonel Reynolds's reverse. He barked at Frog.

"What does Colonel Reynolds want now?"

"Sir." Frog was still out of breath. "Several thousands of the enemy are encamped over the far side of the ridge from Colonel Reynolds, in the valley of the Little Bighorn River. Colonel Reynolds seeks your orders?"

"Orders!" bellowed Custer with such force that the tent in which they were standing seemed to be carried up into the air. "An officer who waits for orders while the enemy is massing in front of him. . . . Orders, damn it! This isn't a parade: this is war."

Frog couldn't think of what comment to make, so very sensibly he kept quiet. The General thundered on.

"I'll give Colonel Reynolds orders all right. Tell him he is relieved from his command. Tell him to go training horses in some depot back in the east. Tell him I'm sending General Crook to take over. Crook!" he roared. "Send General Crook to me."

General Crook as a Brigadier-General was the next ranking officer after Custer, and the two men were as alike as chalk is to cheese. Crook was a methodical little man, with a bald head, greying moustache, whose voice was scarcely louder than a whisper. He was an excellent quartermaster; because of his powers of organization he had been steadily promoted over the heads of more dashing soldiers.

General Crook did not exactly like the idea of taking over command from a demoted officer. It all seemed very untidy. He hated rushing things, but he was too well disciplined to challenge his orders—and he knew Custer too well to think of trying to talk him into some other plan.

After a few hours' sleep Crook rode off with a small party, including Frog. On the way the Brigadier put a string of questions to Frog. He wanted to know exactly how many Indians he had seen, what they were doing, the position of their tents, the number of their animals. When the detailed cross-examination was over, he asked Frog why he had come to the conclusion that the Indians were likely to attack.

"After all, it might be some sort of palaver. Or they might be celebrating a chief's marriage."

Frog was surprised at such a question. It seemed so obvious that the Red Indians had gathered together with hostile intentions that he could not produce a convincing answer.

Crook was far from impressed.

"You are the scout who failed to spot Fleet Foot's ambush, aren't you?" he said with a quiet sarcasm that made Frog feel even worse than after Custer's anger. "Very well. We shall see what the Redskins are up to before doing anything further."

Crook ended the conversation and turned his thoughts to the unpleasant task of how he was going to tell Colonel Reynolds that he was relieved. In the end he worked out that he would do wisest by leaving Reynolds in nominal command, saying that Custer had sent him to carry out a reconnaisance in force, using Reynolds' men for the job. After all, Reynolds was a fairly decent fellow with a good record of service, and Custer's temper was notorious. If Custer insisted on relieving him, let him carry out the sacking himself.

Reynolds turned out to be more than happy that Crook should take over the situation: he was glad to be rid of the responsibility. Crook lost no time. He divided up the men into five equal detachments: four were to advance around the flanks in different directions to explore the enemy's intentions, the fifth was to guard the baggage.

Frog was placed in the base detachment, having done more than his fill of riding in the last two days. Most of the men gathered round in groups, playing cards. Crook sat in his tent writing a long report of the situation. Reynolds went on exercising his charger as if nothing had happened. Frog sat down by the fire. It was a poor fire. He got hold of a blanket and started to fan it.

"Hi there, Jean!" shouted one of the card players. "Stop making such a beastly draught."

"Sorry!" Frog was genuinely apologetic. He stopped fanning so energetically, got hold of three big sticks with which to make a tripod in the centre of the fire and bring the blanket over the top. The others paid no more attention to him. From time to time Frog removed the blanket and the smoke belched up into the sky. It was about an hour before the flames devoured the sticks making the tripod. Frog rescued the blanket as it fell on the burning embers, just in time to prevent it catching light.

*　　*　　*　　*　　*

Wild Horse rode up and down the long rows of tents that stretched for four miles down the bank of the Little Bighorn. Here and there he dismounted to give some chief an instruction from the commander-in-chief, Sitting Bull. Back in the saddle, he stared relentlessly at the range of mountains over the other side of the river. Suddenly he pulled on the reins to turn his horse, and trotted back to where Sitting Bull squatted, surrounded by a number of medicine men.

Sitting Bull had the decisiveness of a true general: he listened to Wild Horse, gave out a string of orders. Within five minutes a hundred Redskins were down by the water's edge getting into canoes.

In another two hours the Redskins had crossed the mountain barrier. "Halt!" shouted their leader. He darted forward on tiptoe. What were the white men doing? He rubbed his eyes. Yes, they were not deceiving him. The American soldiers were sprawling on the ground in little groups, playing cards. There was only one sentry, and he was polishing his nails.

The leader waved his men on. Swiftly, silently, they disposed of the sentry. A knife went through his ribs, and a hand covered his mouth to prevent him from screaming. They left his body and ran on towards the clearing.

As they broke out on to the open ground the braves started shouting the war cries of their ancestors. The soldiers jumped up, but it was too late. The Indian arrows fell with devastating accuracy, each one finding its mark.

The soldiers were in confusion. Crook was writing in his tent, Reynolds was away in the woods exercising his horse. Some of the troops put up their hands, but there was no question of the Indians accepting surrender. They did not know the meaning of "hands up"; they thought that the white men were calling on their gods for help, and so determined to slaughter them on the spot before the gods could have time to come.

The Americans were hopelessly outnumbered. They fought on as best they could. But it was Colonel Reynolds who saved the day. He rode back to the clearing as fast as his horse would gallop. He pulled up to survey the scene. It was an appalling sight. The ground was littered with the bodies of his men. The few that survived were fighting at close quarters. They were putting up a brave resistance, but they had not a chance.

The noise of the battle was terrifying. On top of the Indian shouts, the American guns and the cries of the wounded, the air reverberated with the neighing of panic-struck horses. The cavalry horses were tethered in a circle to the trees at the edge of the clearing. Unable to escape, condemned to watch their masters' death, they became as wild as elephants amok.

Reynolds saw a chance. Throwing down his rifle, he drew his cavalry sword, and turned his horse away to the outside of the clearing. With all the skill of a circus turn he cantered round past each tethered rope and, as he passed, he slashed his sword down to cut the tie.

The freed animals were still possessed with the same mad fear. Loosed from their ropes, they galloped riderless into the fray around the camp-fire, knocking over red and white men in their path. The chaos that followed gave the Americans time enough to extricate themselves: the survivors threw themselves up on to the bare backs of their horses and rode them away to the woods, clutching on to the hair of the mane. The wounded and dead were abandoned.

General Crook had been spared from a surprise death since he was writing in his tent when the Indians fell to the attack. From the cover of the tent flap he fired volley after volley at the attackers until they clinched hand to hand, knife to knife, with his soldiers, and then regretfully he had had to lower his smoking gun.

Now he was cut off, abandoned and forgotten. Only Frog, who happened to be away walking in the woods when the battle began, thought of Brigadier-General Crook. He rushed up to Colonel Reynolds and asked permission to go back to fetch General Crook.

"How will you go, Trooper?"

"On your horse, if you'll lend him, sir."

"Very well," nodded the Colonel. "Hold the reins while I dismount. I want to give her a few lumps of sugar. All right, laddie, up you jump! How the deuce you'll get hold of him, I don't know. Why, he must have a couple of dozen knives sticking into him by now. Still, see what you can do."

Frog's task proved to be quite easy. As he guided the charger round the trees he was working out to himself how he might save the General. His clever plan was never needed. The Indians had made off by the time he reached the camp, carrying with them the scalps of their dead foes. They had not bothered to search the tents, else they might have been able to take back the prize scalp of a general.

Frog found General Crook seated once again at his table, writing a report. He had started on a clean sheet of paper, recounting the casualties suffered by the forces under his command. The idea of retreating to safety did not occur to him.

He was, as has been said, a methodical man. He would not allow such little interruptions as an Indian attack to change his plans. He told Frog that he had every intention of staying just where he was until his scouting detachments reported back.

"However, Trooper," he said, picking up his pen, "I am not insensible to your action in coming back to fetch me. I shall recommend you in my dispatch to General Custer for an immediate decoration."

"Gee, thank you, sir." Frog was really delighted. General Custer would learn that he was to be trusted.

"And, Trooper"—General Crook looked up from his paper—"kindly ask Colonel Reynolds to round up the survivors and have them report back here."

"Yessir!" Frog saluted smartly.

Out of the fifty men originally detailed to the base detachment seventeen lived to report back for duty. It was a stunning victory for the Redskins, an ignominious defeat for the White Man. Back at the Indians' camp the news was celebrated with the frenzied banging of war drums, and dancing went on through the night. Crook, when he went out of his tent for a tour of inspection before turning in, watched the flicker of the countless Indian fires reflected as a pink glow in the sky. Another man might have been afraid: not Crook; the noise of the drums and the colour of the sky were to him just matters of observation to be noted down in his day-book when he returned to his tent.

The news of the disaster reached General Custer the next morning. He took it angrily. He cursed his officers. He declared that he was the most pitiable commander in the American Army for he was served by no one but timid fools.

"I sent General Crook to attack," he shouted, "and all he does it to sit in his tent until the enemy surprises him. There's nothing for it but for me to put some courage into my officers: they've got none of their own!"

Custer ordered his men to a fast trot. There was no time to be lost. By nightfall he had joined up with the body of men under General Crook. He questioned the leaders of the scouting parties sent out by Crook. Each one reported that the Redskins were gathered in a strength of several thousands. There had never been such an army of braves in living memory. All the clans of the Sioux were there—the Brulés, the Minneconjous, the Sans Arcs, the Oglalas, the Uncpapas and the Black Feet. So were several other Redskin nations—the Cheyennes and the Arapahos.

"I just don't believe it." Custer strode up and down within the narrow confines of his tent. "You men are in a blue funk. Whoever heard of the Sioux getting together with the Cheyenne?"

"I have assembled all the information brought in, sir," Crook spoke quietly, "and there appears to be no doubt that the Redskins have managed to form a wide alliance of all the nations in the north-western territories."

"Stuff and nonsense." Custer would have none of it. "Maybe a few tribes have got together for a joint hunting expedition."

"I thought of that myself, sir." Crook was not in the least put out. "That is why I sent out scouts to discover the Indians' intentions. They were ordered to enter into parleys, but it was quite useless. Our men were shot at before ever they could get near enough even to shout."

"The more fool you, Crook, trusting an Indian. Why, the blighters will always shoot at you unless you are in considerably greater numbers than they are!"

Crook did not rise to the insult. "That is just our difficulty, sir. We are outnumbered at least five times."

"You've said that before." Custer had made up his mind not to accept the reports. "In my view the whole lot of you are just trying to explain away the licking that you've taken by telling me that there are swarms upon swarms of Redskins over the other side of the mountains. I just don't believe you. And that's that." There was nothing more to be said.

In a moment Custer was talking again.

"Tell you what. Send me that lynx-eyed half-Indian lad. I thought the fellow was no good, but Crook seems to have formed a different opinion. I'll send the lad off on his own. He can dress up as an Indian. He looks like one. No one will notice the difference. Then he can count up exactly how many of the blighters that there are and find out what they are up to."

Frog thought it wisest to say no more than "Yes, sir" at the end of the General's orders. Custer was in full swing. Without bothering to dismiss Frog he started issuing more orders. Captain Benteen with 125 men was to go up the next valley behind the Little Bighorn to seal off the Indians' retreat. Custer would advance with his remaining force to the river, whereupon Major Reno was to take a raiding party across the water and go into the attack. Custer would carry along the near bank for a few miles before crossing. Then he would come in on Reno's flank and fold up the enemy.

Frog slipped out of the tent. Custer had lost all interest in him. Somewhere in the baggage train there was a heap of Red Indian clothes captured in previous engagements, used by the Americans as presents to bribe friendly Indians. A chief would be given a fine feathered head-dress, an Indian who worked making a bridge for the wagon train might be rewarded with a pipe.

Frog fitted himself out so realistically that he was twice arrested while going through the American camp: he had only got himself released because he spoke English and knew the password. Slogging up the mountainside, he whistled contentedly to himself—this was his great chance.

It was twelve hours later that he returned to camp, exhausted but very satisfied. He was taken straight to General Custer's tent.

"Heh!" the General exclaimed. "So you've come back. No trouble, I hope."

"No, sir," Frog explained. "I was able to make my way into the Arapaho tents. It was dark, and no one noticed me sitting round the camp-fire. I left as soon as the dawn came up."

"Good lad." Custer smacked his hands together. "Now what did you find out?"

"There are meetings going on between the various Indian nations, sir. That is why they have gathered together."

"What the devil are they meeting about?" Custer inquired tersely.

"I think they are trying to reach some agreement about dividing up their hunting-grounds fairly."

General Crook broke in quietly. "That does not tie up with our other reports."

Frog hastily covered himself. "I couldn't be quite sure. You see, sir, I was only listening to casual talk around the fire."

"Yes, yes." Custer was eager to get on to the question of how many Indians there were.

"I should put their strength at around four thousand, sir."

"What's that?" Custer's voice showed traces of annoyance.

"That would be just about correct," said Crook, looking down at a sheet of paper covered with calculations.

"There were four thousand, sir," Frog continued, "but there won't be now. Gall, the war chief of the Sioux, is taking his men away this morning. They are going back to their hunting-grounds."

"The very moment to attack," Custer shouted. "Reno, get your men on the move at once. You are to cross the river at daybreak tomorrow. By that time Benteen's men will be dealing with Mr. Gall and his Sioux."

"If I might put in a word." Crook had gone so far as to get up from his folding chair.

"Don't!" bawled Custer. "I know you were right. There were four thousand of them. But there aren't now: and that's what matters."

"But the evidence, sir, all points to——"

"Oh, be hanged with your evidence! This isn't a law court; it is advanced headquarters of the U.S. 7th Cavalry."

Custer strode out of the tent.

* * * * *

Wild Horse sat next to Sitting Bull at the war council of the chiefs. Squatting round in a circle were all the great warriors of the Indian nations—Fleet Foot, Big Road and Red Horse; Gall, Lame Deer and Hump of the Sioux and the famous Two Moon. In the centre was a rough map of the river region drawn with blood on a buffalo hide. Sitting Bull was speaking.

"We shall let the Americans advance across the river and come forward from the bank. Then, when they think that we shall not offer serious resistance, I shall give the order to shoot. Our bowmen will be posted out of sight. At the sign a shower of arrows will rain upon the White Man."

The braves made their plans carefully. Each tribe of each nation was given its allotted task. Each chief knew the pass-word. Returned to their own people from the council of war, the chiefs passed the word down the ranks: it was a word they repeated in awe—"Revenge".

Revenge, revenge. As the sentries peered out into the night their muscles tensed, their pulses quickened. As the braves polished the tips of their spears and tightened the strings of their bows, they boasted of how many white men each would kill on the next day. They spoke of the blood that would flow in such plenty that the Little Bighorn River would be coloured red. They spoke of the sea, too: the sea which none of them had ever seen, the sea which would turn red, too, when the water of the Little Bighorn poured into its midst.

Few of them felt like sleep. They sang their war songs, they danced their war dances. They ate a great meal of buffalo meat, such a meal as normally would last a week in rations. With the first pale shimmer of morning showing over the mountain-tops they broke off whatever they were doing and ran to their posts. The river bank was cleared. The tents were taken down and removed into the woods. The carcasses of the buffaloes they had eaten were scattered over the grass to give the impression that the Indians had abandoned camp and gone.

Sitting Bull was in command of the ambush. Wild Horse led the body of men that marched down the river. Before the light was good enough to see across the water Wild Horse was already two miles downstream. When Major Reno, leading the vanguard of the U.S. 7th Cavalry, reached the water's edge, there was nothing to be seen. He sent a rider back to General Custer with the news. Ten minutes later the General reined in his horse beside Reno.

"Looks as if they've all packed up," the General decided. "Suppose the others thought that they'd go off with the Sioux. Blessed nuisance. Thought we'd catch 'em sitting. Still, there are a few fires yet burning. The blighters can't be far away."

"Most likely they have gone downstream, sir," suggested Reno.

"Wouldn't be surprised. We'll keep to the original plan, Reno. You cross now, get over there and find out which way they've gone. You'll be able to see by their tracks, and then send a message over to me. Meanwhile I'll take the main body downstream, ready to head them off. There's probably a ford somewhere lower down where we can get over on horseback."

Reno gave the orders, and canoes were brought down to the water. It meant leaving the horses behind. If there was nothing doing on the other side he would have the horses brought over by raft. The paddle across was uneventful enough. Reno went ahead with a couple of sergeants: they kicked the smouldering ashes with their feet. There was nothing much to be discovered —only the usual debris left in a deserted camp.

Reno waved on the rest of his men. He was going to reconnoitre. Six groups of six men were to go out to look for tracks downstream or into the forest. He wanted to know just which way the Redskins had gone. He would go with the downstream party. That seemed the likeliest bet.

Sitting Bull sucked in air through his teeth as his eyes followed every movement of the White Man. He could not afford to allow them to break up into small detachments: he wanted a big sitting target for his bowmen. Around his neck strung by a lace of hide was a horn of bone. With a sharp flourish he brought the horn to his mouth and blew with all his strength.

The noise carried across the river. Custer turned round to Crook, who was riding on his right.

"What's that?"

"An Indian horn," said Crook without hesitation.

"Must be some of the blighters there, after all." Custer gazed across the water, but from where he was there was nothing out of the ordinary to be seen. "Guess Reno can tackle them. Come on, let's find a crossing quick and get over there to see what's doing."

Reno had no time to think what the horn might be. A deluge of arrows as heavy as a hail storm fell around him.

"Form square!" he yelled.

The soldiers huddled themselves into as small a target as they could. The horn blew again. And now the Indians charged, screaming and shouting, their spears brandished above their heads.

"Fire!" Reno commanded.

The leading Redskins tottered and fell. But their places were filled by others.

"Fire! Fire! Fire!" Reno's throat strained to the depth to carry his voice over the din.

Custer swore and cursed when he heard the sound of firing. Why couldn't he find a ford? He smelled blood, and he wanted to be in on the kill.

"Crook, pull out your maps. Damn it, man, there must be a ford."

Crook spread the maps out over their saddles. But there was nothing to be seen. The Little Bighorn was marked as a dotted line running through an uncharted range of mountains.

"I would advise you to ferry the horses across, sir."

"Waste of time." Custer's face was getting redder. "Come on, let's go down another mile. There's bound to be a ford before far. Come on!" He shook the reins and dug in his spurs.

Meanwhile Reno's men were fighting desperately. They were running low in ammunition, but the bullets which they had spent seemed to have taken no effect. It was as if the words of the prophet had come true. The Indians charged right into the rifle mouths again and again. They seemed to be without fear. Even the wounded carried on with the blood pouring down their skins, seemingly without pain. Only the crumpled bodies here and there showed that the White Man's bullets had not lost all their power.

"Jean!" Reno called out in the middle of the din. "You and Murphy get back to the river, if you possibly can. Fetch some ammunition from the other side. And tell General Custer to come quickly. We can't hold out much longer even with ammo."

The two men worked their way to the back flank of the square. While the Indians were charging the front and sides, they made a dash for the river bank. It was a quarter of a mile away. Frog made it. Murphy went down with an arrow through the back of his neck.

Frog jumped into one of the canoes that had been left drawn up on the sandy shelf. Madly he paddled across. Once on the far side he threw himself on the grass heaving like an hysterical child. He was "out" for the count, he thought. He must have been wounded. Jerkily he felt round his body, expecting to find the warm, squelchiness of blood. But he could find nothing out of the ordinary. Just before the referee called "ten", he jumped up with the freshness of a boxer eager to have his own back before the end of the round. Seizing one of the waiting horses, he rode off at full speed.

Meanwhile Custer was growing angrier. He could not find a ford no matter how far he went downstream. The sound of gunfire was dying.

"Damn it!" He swung his horse round to face the column behind him. "Halt!" The troopers pulled up their animals. They too were getting edgy after spending three hours, without breakfast, nosing down the river edge looking for a ford, stopping and starting again all the time.

"We're going to ferry the horses over," Custer announced. "I am going to take a forward party of 'A', 'B' and 'C' troops over by canoe. General Crook will bring over the horses just as quick as he can assemble the rafts."

Scarcely had he spoken, when over the other side of the water Wild Horse led his men out from behind the trees. The Indians had been following Custer all that morning, keeping away out of sight behind the wood.

Crook immediately ordered the men left to him with the transport party to take up defensive position and fire.

"Fire, hell!" shouted Custer. "I'm crossing. So are you. Get moving."

The men dragged the canoes into the water with Custer behind them urging them on.

"Faster, man."

"Get into that canoe. Now steady it. I am coming in."

The canoe rocked, but righted itself.

Half a dozen boats set out together, the men in them paddling as fast as they knew how. As they drew near the bank on the other side Wild Horse ordered his bowmen to open fire. The arrows rained down. Custer leaped on to the sand; his revolver was blazing.

"Don't stop. Fire as you run!"

Wild Horse ordered his men to charge.

Twenty yards from the shore Custer's first boatloads of cavalrymen wrestled with the Redskin braves. It was wrist upon wrist, knee against knee—no holds barred—who could get his weapon home first. Custer slammed his Bowie knife through the chest of an Indian: he wrenched it out again with a flick of the wrist and plunged it into the back of another.

But it was hopeless. Wild Horse's braves were everywhere. They were even on the bank of the river, standing firing at the next boatloads crossing the water.

Custer could see the position. If Wild Horse could turn back the oncoming canoes, then he and his few soldiers would be cut off and surrounded. At all costs he must give the men in the canoes a chance.

"Break away! Back!" he ordered.

The Indians were surprised at the sudden retreat. Custer dodged back to the river bank. He fired at the bowmen from the bank. One, two, three . . . they swayed and fell *splosh* into the river. Wild Horse was furious. Brandishing a spear in each arm he came running at the white men like a railway engine down the track. The massacre was horrible. But the boats drew up on the sand. Of Custer's first party only he and two more men were alive. Brave as he was, he realized that he had to retreat.

"Stay where you are, boys," he commanded. "We are coming with you." And with that he took a running leap into one of the canoes. His companions followed suit. The men at the paddles realized what was happening. They back-watered as hard as they could out into the current.

Crook realized the situation, too. He was standing on the other bank, supervising the mule parties. As soon as there were no more Americans left on the far shore he gave the order to fire. A hundred men, rifles levelled on their knees make a powerful force. A hail of lead whistled across the river. The Indian bowmen—for all that the prophet had said—crumpled up, wounded, dying and dead. Their ranks gave and broke: they raced back to the cover of the woods.

Custer brought his boats back safely. The wounded were carried out, laid on the ground, and their wounds were washed.

Reno's men fought gallantly on, five miles upstream. Their numbers grew less. The square was more or less a fortification built out of the corpses of the men already dead. No ammunition appeared. Reno could understand why Custer did not come; during occasional breaks in the Indian attacks he could catch the sound of firing being blown up the river.

Frog must have gone down, too, like Murphy, thought Reno. I suppose they got him with one of their arrows while he was in a canoe. Poor lad! He was a good soldier and a good scout. He sighed. His own chances of surviving that day were growing thin. They must break square and run for the river. He waited for a lull in the firing to give the order.

Of Reno's men but a third survived that crossing back. All

251

the wounded had to be abandoned on the other side. Their piteous requests for help made Reno feel like standing there on the bank and fighting it out. But he had no right to sacrifice the men still alive. He tossed his whisky flask to one of the wounded, his spare knife he gave to another. And then he flung himself into a canoe and picked up the paddle.

By three in the afternoon both Reno and Custer had been driven back across the Little Bighorn. They were five miles apart. In after years Custer was to be blamed for having allowed Reno's men to go down against tremendous odds while he marched away along the river. Some historians have made out that Custer deliberately left Reno to his disaster. Nothing could be less true. Custer may have been impetuous and bad-tempered, but he was brave and loyal, too. He wanted nothing more than to get across the river and come to Reno's aid. But being a cavalryman he wanted to take his horses with him. And that was how the tragedy set in: there was no horse ford.

Driven back, dazed, Custer prepared for another crossing. Following the text-books of war, he moved down the river to a bend. He posted rifles on each flank of the bend to cover the tongue of projecting land with a withering fire as soon as the first landing party could reach the far bank.

Had Frog arrived with Reno's message, then Custer would surely have turned about and marched upstream. But Frog, although he mounted a horse, never came with the dispatch. History perhaps is unfair to Custer. He still believed that Reno was on the far side when he started on his second, more elaborate, crossing.

As it turned out, Custer had scarcely placed his troops for the new attempt to cross when they caught the cries of Indians approaching. Sitting Bull had sent a large force across the river under Chief Two Moon: he had ordered it to cross half-way between Reno and Custer. Now the two American forces were separated by over two thousand Indians. Custer was outnumbered five times.

With their backs to the river the Americans could not have been in a worse position for a stand. Custer rallied his men. He ordered them to move quickly to a small hill a quarter of a mile inland, a foot-hill of the mountain range. Those who could seized horses, but many of the animals had panicked and

*He rallied his men on a hill shouting
"Stand men! Stand and fight!"*

strayed. Had all the men got horses they might have made a getaway (though Custer would have been the last commander to order a general retreat).

Custer was no quitter. He rallied his men in a square on the hill, shouting: "Stand, men! Stand and fight!" He seized hold of the flag of the 7th Cavalry and rammed its staff into the crest.

"Shoulder to shoulder, men!" he roared. "There is no retreat."

The tale of the last stand of General George Armstrong Custer and his force of 12 officers and 238 men throughout that night of 25 June 1876 has often been told. It is one of the most glorious pages of American history. Every American schoolchild knows it, just as every English child repeats the Charge of the Light Brigade. Both episodes were equally ill-starred: both showed how brave men can be when fighting fearful odds.

All that night long Custer and his men defended their lives and their flag. The Indians showered arrows, charged with spears, flung tomahawks, whirled their pogamogan clubs. One after another the Americans fell. But so long as one man lived, so long as one round of ammunition was unfired, no Indian reached the summit of that hill. When the sun rose high up into the sky on the next day, it shone on a hill covered with the bodies of paleface and Redskin, side by side, often one on top of another. The flag no longer flew. Wild Horse was standing on the crest with both his hands raised to the heavens. He was crying out:

"No longer shall you suffer, oh my fathers! We have killed the White Man in his thousands. In your thousands are you free."

Five miles away Reno was saved from a similar massacre by the timely arrival of Benteen, who had heard the sound of firing and returned with his 125 men. Even so, Reno lost all but twenty of his troopers. And Benteen's force was badly cut about before they managed to pull out Reno's survivors and get them mounted behind, two on a saddle.

It was these remnants who crossed the mountains to tell the tale of the most crushing defeat ever suffered by the White Man at the hands of the Redskin.

Wild Horse chanted to the heavens. The braves came around him. They brought the drums. They beat out the news, and back came the thuds of Sitting Bull's drums, announcing that he had driven the White Man headlong into retreat, that the plain was littered with their bodies.

Suddenly the braves turned. A lone American soldier was galloping towards them. Instinctively they raised their bows.

"Don't shoot!" Wild Horse ordered sharply.

They lowered their bows. As the rider came they drew back to allow him to pass. He leapt off his charger at Wild Horse's feet. Frog opened his arms, and so did Wild Horse.

"We are revenged," gasped Frog, closing his arms around Wild Horse's shiny, red-brown chest.

"We are revenged for the massacre of Sand Creek," answered Wild Horse, hugging Frog to him.

"When the paleskins turned us away from their fort without food in the winter," the braves chanted.

"When the paleskins betrayed us and massacred our brothers in the night."

Their voices rose to a crescendo of triumph.

"Long hair, you have found what you were seeking—Death!"

"Long hair, you have found what you were seeking—Death!"